PEPTIDES AND AMINO ACIDS

THE ORGANIC CHEMISTRY MONOGRAPH SERIES

Ronald Breslow, EDITOR

Columbia University

ORGANIC REACTION MECHANISMS

Ronald Breslow

Columbia University

THE MOLECULES OF NATURE

James Hendrickson

Brandeis University

MODERN SYNTHETIC REACTIONS

Herbert House

Massachusetts Institute of Technology

INTRODUCTION TO STEREOCHEMISTRY

Kurt Mislow

Princeton University

■PEPTIDES AND AMINO ACIDS

KENNETH D. KOPPLE ILLINOIS INSTITUTE OF TECHNOLOGY

W. A. BENJAMIN, INC. ■ New York Amsterdam

1966

PEPTIDES AND AMINO ACIDS

Library of Congress Catalog Card Number 66–12701
Manufactured in the United States of America

*The manuscript was put into production on 7 July 1965;
this volume was published on 15 February 1966*

W. A. BENJAMIN, INC., *New York, New York 10016*

▪ EDITOR'S FOREWORD

UNDERGRADUATE EDUCATION in chemistry is in the midst of a major revolution. Sophisticated material, including extensive treatments of current research problems, is increasingly being introduced into college chemistry courses. In organic chemistry, this trend is apparent in the new "elementary" textbooks. However, it has become clear that a single text, no matter how sophisticated, is not the best medium for presenting glimpses of advanced material in addition to the necessary basic chemistry. A spirit of critical evaluation of the evidence is essential in an advanced presentation, while "basic" material must apparently be presented in a relatively dogmatic fashion.

Accordingly, we have instituted a series of short monographs intended as supplements to a first-year organic text; they may, of course, be used either concurrently or subsequently. It is our hope that teachers of beginning organic chemistry courses will supplement the usual text with one or more of these intermediate level monographs and that they may find use in secondary courses as well. In general, the books are designed to be read independently by the interested student and to lead him into the current research literature. It is hoped that they will serve their intended educational purpose and will help the student to recognize organic chemistry as the vital and exciting field it is.

We welcome any comments or suggestions about the series.

RONALD BRESLOW

New York, New York
December, 1964

▪ PREFACE

LIKE OTHER SPECIALIZED TOPICS in organic chemistry, peptide chemistry is treated only briefly in undergraduate courses and texts. To satisfy any deeper interest, students must jump from general organic texts to specialized review articles and the research literature. This brief book is intended to bridge that gap. It will thereby, I hope, reduce the activation barrier for entry into this increasingly exciting field.

While retaining the outlook of an organic chemist, I have tried to provide a survey that includes some of the biological and physical chemical aspects of the study of peptides, so that the over-all significance of the area is apparent. This attempt, coupled with limitations on space, has precluded coverage of individual topics in the depth that would warrant citation of the original literature; the references given at the end of each chapter are to recent detailed reviews, although individual papers are cited in a few cases.

I would like to express my appreciation to Professor Murray Goodman and to Mr. Edward A. Dratz, whose comments on the manuscript have led to clearer presentation. The responsibility for the choice of material is, of course, mine.

K. D. KOPPLE

Chicago, Illinois
July 1965

vii

▪ CONTENTS

1

▪ INTRODUCTION

THREE KINDS of organic polymers are elaborated by living organisms. These substances, often called *biopolymers*, perform vital functions. *Nucleic acids* store and copy information necessary for replication of an organism. *Proteins* function as structural materials, act in the biological conversion of chemical to mechanical energy, and catalyze and direct the chemical reactions necessary for growth and maintenance of the living state. *Polysaccharides* serve as structural materials and reservoirs of fuel.

The term protein (derived from the Greek, *proteios*, meaning prime) was appropriately applied, in 1838, to a group of complex nitrogen-containing substances found in plant and animal tissue. At the beginning of the present century, it was recognized that proteins are composed of α-amino carboxylic acids:

combined, by biological processes resulting in the elimination of water, to form polyamides:

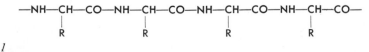

The term *peptide bond* was applied to the amide link between amino acid residues, and molecules composed of α-amino acids so linked are called *peptides*. (The word protein refers to naturally occurring peptides containing more than about 50 amino acid residues in a single molecule.)

Although the molecular backbone of a protein is composed of the same repeating unit, —N—C—CO—, the side chains attached to the saturated carbon atom of each unit vary. Nature has chosen these side chains from a limited number, about 20. Since proteins are generally composed of hundreds of amino acid residues, these 20 building blocks may be arrayed in an infinite number of combinations, each defining a molecule with a particular set of chemical and physical properties. Thus, proteins can be generated with specific tailoring to the biological functions they perform.

In recent years, chemical and biological studies of proteins and related substances have begun to show some details of the dependence of biological function on chemical structure. This has come about through development of chemical and physical methods for determining the structure and chemical reactivity of proteins, and through continued improvement of the synthetic techniques by which protein-like model substances can be rationally prepared. It is the purpose of the following pages to provide an introduction to this chemistry.

In the succeeding chapters, we shall discuss, first, the organic chemistry of the protein building blocks, the amino acids (Chapter 2), then the chemical methods by which these substances can be linked to form peptides (Chapter 3). Many physiologically active peptides, such as hormones and antibiotics, are synthetically accessible. Synthesis serves as a check on proposed structures and as a means for producing potentially useful structural variations. Synthetic peptides are also useful for study of some of the properties of proteins.

In Chapter 4 we discuss the manner in which amino acid sequence and other covalent features of proteins are uncovered. Determination of peptide sequence is now a common, if arduous, procedure, and the order of amino acids in any protein can be determined if enough of it can be isolated in a state of high purity. However, knowledge of the covalent structure alone by no means explains the physical and chemical properties of a peptide. A variety of noncovalent interactions among the peptide backbone, the various side chains, and the environment contribute to the establishment of a favored three-dimensional structure. This is discussed in Chapter 5. In Chapter 6 are cited some examples of areas in which there is a growing knowledge of the relationship between chemical structure of peptides and their biological function.

Synthesis of large peptides and determination of protein structure would not be possible without effective methods for separating amino acid and peptide mixtures into their components. These techniques are presented in the Appendix.

References

The two works listed contain excellent and detailed surveys of most of the topics outlined in succeeding pages.

J. P. Greenstein and M. Winitz, *Chemistry of the Amino Acids,* (3 vols), Wiley, New York, 1961.

H. Neurath (ed.), *The Proteins,* 2nd ed., Vols. I and II, Academic Press, New York, 1963, 1964.

2

▪ α−AMINO ACIDS

2–1 Occurrence

IN PRINCIPLE, the term *amino acid* could be used to refer to any compound containing an amino group and an acidic function. In practice, the words are most often used with reference to the amino acids that have received most intensive study: α-amino carboxylic acids isolated from natural sources. Well over 100 of these have been isolated and identified, but only 20 are obtained upon hydrolysis of typical proteins.

The 20 α-amino acids that are the building blocks of proteins are listed in the first part of Table 2–1. Most of them contain primary amino groups. All but glycine contain at least one asymmetrically substituted atom, the α-carbon, and occur naturally in optically active form. Residues of most occur in all proteins, although hydroxylysine and hydroxyproline appear only in collagen, which is the major protein of skin, bone, tendon, and other connective tissue. Aspartic and glutamic acids, common constituents of all proteins, often appear as the amides asparagine and glutamine. Cystine and cysteine, because of their ready interconvertibility by oxidation-reduction, are considered derivatives of the same substance; cystine is the form usually isolated. Table 2–2 indicates the amino acid composition of several representative proteins from animal sources.

4

TABLE 2–1 ▪

Naturally Occurring α-Amino Acids

Name	Structural formula	Abbreviation
	Protein Building Blocks	
Alanine	$CH_3CH(NH_2)COOH$	Ala
Arginine	$HN{=}C(NH_2)NH(CH_2)_3CH(NH_2)COOH$	Arg
Aspartic acid	$HO{-}COCH_2CH(NH_2)COOH$	Asp
(Asparagine)	$(H_2N{-})$	$Asp(NH_2)$
Cysteine	$HSCH_2CH(NH_2)COOH$	Cys
(Cystine)	$\{SCH_2CH(NH_2)COOH\}_2$	Cys
		$\mid$
		Cys
Glutamic acid	$HO{-}COCH_2CH_2CH(NH_2)COOH$	Glu
(Glutamine)	$(H_2N{-})$	$Glu(NH_2)$
Glycine	$CH_2(NH_2)COOH$	Gly

Histidine

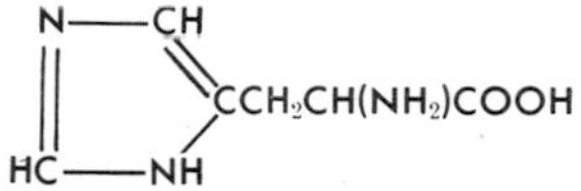

His

Hydroxylysine $H_2NCH_2CH(OH)CH_2CH_2CH(NH_2)COOH$ Hylys

Hydroxyproline

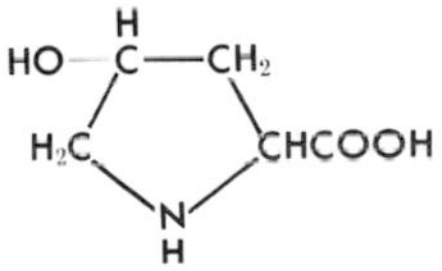

Hypro

Isoleucine	$C_2H_5CH(CH_3)CH(NH_2)COOH$	Ile
Leucine	$(CH_3)_2CHCH_2CH(NH_2)COOH$	Leu
Lysine	$H_2N(CH_2)_4CH(NH_2)COOH$	Lys
Methionine	$CH_3SCH_2CH_2CH(NH_2)COOH$	Met
Phenylalanine	$C_6H_5CH_2CH(NH_2)COOH$	Phe
Proline	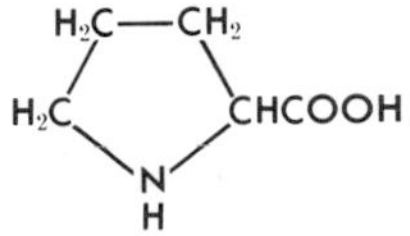	Pro

Serine	$HOCH_2CH(NH_2)COOH$	Ser
Threonine	$CH_3CH(OH)CH(NH_2)COOH$	Thr
Tryptophan	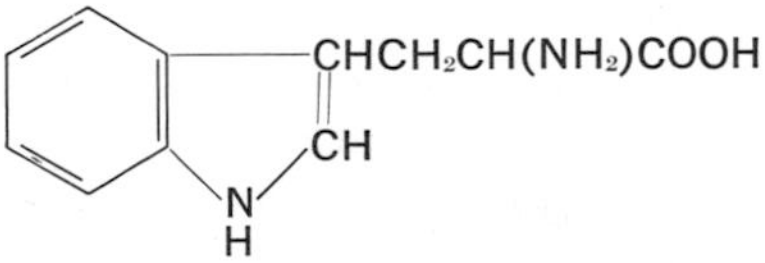	Try

Tyrosine	$p{-}HOC_6H_5CH_2CH(NH_2)COOH$	Tyr
Valine	$(CH_3)_2CHCH(NH_2)COOH$	Val

TABLE 2–1 (*Continued*)

Name	Structural formula	Abbreviation
	Important Nonprotein Amino Acids	
α-Aminoadipic acid	$HOCO(CH_2)_3CH(NH_2)COOH$	Higher plants, antibiotics
α,γ-Diaminobutyric acid	$H_2NCH_2CH_2CH(NH_2)COOH$	Antibiotics
Ornithine	$H_2N(CH_2)_3CH(NH_2)COOH$	Widespread
Pipecolic acid		Higher plants
Sarcosine	CH_3NHCH_2COOH	Widespread
Triiodothyronine (Thyroxine)		Thyroid hormones

Of the proteins listed, keratin and myosin are fibrous proteins, keratin the protein of hair and wool, and myosin the major protein of muscle. Serum albumin has a composition representative of soluble proteins.

The natural α-amino acids are colorless, stable, high-melting solids. Most are soluble in water, at least to some extent, and are not soluble in common organic solvents. The amino acids of protein are obtained from protein hydrolyzates; they do not occur in high concentration uncombined. Because cystine and tyrosine are only sparingly soluble in water, they are readily isolated, but separation of other amino acids in pure form requires special techniques. All the amino acids listed in Table 2–1 have been synthesized, most by several different routes.

TABLE 2–2 ▪
Amino Acid Composition of Representative Proteins[a]

	Serum albumin[b]	Collagen[c]	Keratin[d]	Myosin[e]
Ala	8.1	11	5	9
Arg	3.9	4.9	7.1	5
Asp	9.5	4.7	6	9.9
Cys	5.7	0	11.2	1
Glu	12.9	7.4	12.1	18.2
Gly	2.8	32.9	8.2	4.6
His	3	0.15	0.7	1.9
Hylys	0	0.5	0	0
Hypro	0	9.7	0	0
Ile	2.3	0.6	2.8	4.9
Leu	10.8	1.8	6.9	9.4
Lys	10.1	3.0	2.3	10.6
Met	0.6	0.9	0.55	2.7
Phe	4.6	1.2	2.5	3.4
Pro	4.8	12.9	7.5	2.5
Ser	4.7	4.1	10.2	4.5
Thr	5.7	2	6.5	5.1
Try	0.3	0	1.2	0.5
Tyr	3.2	0.4	4.2	2.3
Val	5.8	2.0	5	5

[a] Mole per cent of each amino acid in hydrolyzate.
[b] Bovine.
[c] Rat tail tendon.
[d] Merino wool.
[e] Rabbit skeletal muscle.

2–2 Ionic Properties

Typical α-amino acids are solids that are appreciably soluble only in water; they do not melt until they decompose at almost 300°C. This behavior suggests that they are salt-like molecules. It seems reasonable, therefore, that α-amino acid structures are correctly written in the *dipolar ion* (often called *zwitterion*) form,

$$R—CH—COO^-$$
$$| $$
$$NH_3^+$$

rather than as the uncharged species represented in Table 2–1.

Amino acids can be titrated in aqueous solution, and titration reveals the expected two ionizable groups. These groups have ionization constants of about 10^{-2} (p$K_A \approx 2$) and 10^{-9} (p$K_A \approx 9$) mole/liter. If the dipolar ion represents the structure of a neutral amino acid, the observed ionization reactions are those indicated in Eq. (2-1) and (2-2). According to these equations, the p$K \approx 2$ ionization

$$RCH(NH_3^+)COOH \rightleftharpoons RCH(NH_3^+)COO^- + H^+ \qquad (2-1)$$

$$RCH(NH_3^+)COO^- \rightleftharpoons RCH(NH_2)COO^- + H^+ \qquad (2-2)$$

is that of a carboxyl group, and the p$K \approx 9$ ionization is that of an aliphatic ammonium ion; these pK_A are reasonable values for the groups to which they are assigned. On the other hand, if the nonpolar form of the amino acid were involved in the major ionization equilibria, as in Eqs. (2-3) and (2-4), one would have to assign the

$$RCH(NH_3^+)COOH \rightleftharpoons RCH(NH_2)COOH + H^+ \qquad (2-3)$$

$$RCH(NH_2)COOH \rightleftharpoons RCH(NH_2)COO^- + H^+ \qquad (2-4)$$

p$K \approx 2$ ionization to an aliphatic ammonium ion, and that of p$K \approx 9$ to a carboxylic acid. The latter assignments contradict previous experience with related amines and carboxylic acids.

If there are nonionized amino acid molecules present in an amino acid solution, the ratio of dipolar ions to nonionized molecules is the ratio of the equilibrium constants of Eqs. (2-1) and (2-3), $K_{(2-1)}/K_{(2-3)}$:

$$\frac{K_{(2-1)}}{K_{(2-3)}} = \frac{[RCH(NH_3^+)COO^-][\cancel{H^+}]}{[\cancel{RCH(NH_3^+)COOH}]} \cdot \frac{[\cancel{RCH(NH_3^+)COOH}]}{[\cancel{H^+}][RCH(NH_2)COOH]}$$

An equilibrium constant for Eq. (2-3) cannot be determined directly, but an approximation to it is the measurable ionization of the ammonium form of an α-amino acid ester [Eq. (2-5)]. $K_{(2-5)}$ is about

$$RCH(NH_3^+)COOR \rightleftharpoons RCH(NH_2)COOR + H^+ \qquad (2-5)$$

3×10^{-8} mole/liter (p$K_A \approx 7.5$). Using this value as a replacement for $K_{(2-3)}$, the ratio of dipolar to nonionized forms can be estimated at 10^5. Thus, both titration of α-amino acids in solution and the properties of the solid substances indicate that they exist almost entirely in the dipolar form.

Further confirmation of the dipolar-ion structure is obtained by examination of the vibrational spectra of amino acids. Atoms composing a molecule oscillate about their equilibrium positions, and these oscillations are excited by absorption of electromagnetic radiation of frequencies equal to their natural frequencies of oscillation. Vibrational frequencies lie in the infrared region of the electromagnetic spectrum, and are often characteristic of particular functional groups. One useful set of infrared absorptions are those that excite the oscillation of carbonyl carbon and oxygen atoms along the line joining them. *Carbonyl-stretching absorptions*, as these are called, occur at frequencies corresponding to infrared wavelengths near 6 microns. [Infrared frequencies are usually cited in wave numbers (units of cm⁻¹), the number of oscillations that occur in the time light takes to travel 1 cm. The frequency in wave numbers is numerically equal to 10,000 divided by the wavelength in microns, so that a 6-micron wavelength corresponds to a frequency of 1667 wave numbers.] Amino acids, in the solid state or in neutral solution, do not absorb infrared radiation at 1720 cm⁻¹ (5.8 microns), a frequency that experience has indicated is characteristic of a nonionized carboxyl group. Instead, they exhibit absorptions near 1400 and 1600 cm⁻¹ (7.15 and 6.25 microns), frequencies characteristic of the carboxylate ion; this is consistent with the dipolar-ion structure. In strongly acidic solutions of amino acids, however, the 1720-cm⁻¹ absorption does appear, indicating operation of the carboxyl-carboxylate equilibrium [Eqs. (2–6), (2–1)].

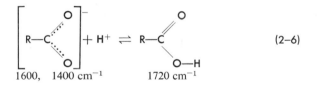

It is worth noting that the pK_A of carboxyl ionization of the simple aliphatic amino acids, for example, glycine and alanine, is about 2.3. In contrast, the pK_A of the corresponding fatty acids, that is, acetic and propionic acids, is about 4.8. In other words, the α-amino acids lose their carboxyl proton 300 times more readily than do fatty acids. The source of this enhanced acidity is the electric field of the nearby positively charged ammonium ion. Presence of this group reduces the work required to remove a proton, with its positive charge, from the adjacent carboxyl group. The magnitude of the effect an ammonium ion has on the ionization of a carboxyl group decreases, as expected, with increasing distance between the two groups. For β-aminopropionic acid the carboxyl pK_A is about 3.6, and for γ-aminobutyric acid it is about 4.2.

Many of the naturally occurring α-amino acids have additional functional groups that may ionize in aqueous solution. Most of these side chain functions exhibit a normal pK_A, as indicated in Table 2–3. Two values are listed in the table for the sulfhydryl groups of cysteine. This is because ionization of this group and the adjacent α-amino group occur in the same pH region. The lower pK_A corresponds to ionization of sulfhydryl adjacent to ammonium:

$$\begin{array}{c} CH_2-CH-COO^- \\ |\qquad | \\ SH\quad NH_3^+ \end{array}$$

the higher to sulfhydryl adjacent to amino:

$$\begin{array}{c} CH_2-CH-COO^- \\ |\qquad | \\ SH\quad NH_2 \end{array}$$

TABLE 2–3 ■

Ionization of Side-Chain Functional Groups

Amino acid	Side-chain ionization	pK_A
Glutamic acid	$-CH_2COOH \rightleftharpoons -CH_2COO^- + H^+$	4.3
Tyrosine	$-CH_2-C_6H_5-OH \rightleftharpoons -CH_2-C_6H_5-O^- + H^+$	10.1
Lysine	$-CH_2NH_3^+ \rightleftharpoons -CH_2NH_2 + H^+$	10.3
Cysteine	$-CH_2SH \rightleftharpoons -CH_2S^- + H^+$	8.5
Arginine	$-CH_2NH-C\overset{{}^+NH_2}{\diagdown_{NH_2}} \rightleftharpoons -CH_2NH-C\overset{NH}{\diagdown_{NH_2}} + H^+$	10.0 13.2
Histidine	(imidazole ionization) $+ H^+$	6.0

2-3 Chemical Reactivity of α-Amino Acids

Much of the chemistry of α-amino acids may be deduced from knowledge of the reactivity of isolated amino and carboxyl groups, if one bears in mind that many carboxylic acid derivatives react with amines to form amides. Those reactions of amino acids important to the synthesis of peptides are discussed in Chapter 3. Some others, characteristic of compounds in which amino and carboxyl groups are attached to the same carbon atom, are discussed below.

α-AMINO ACID ESTERS   Amino acids readily undergo acid-catalyzed esterification if a strong acid is present in excess of the amount required to protonate the amino group. To prepare methyl or ethyl esters, a suspension of the amino acid in excess alcohol is saturated with anhydrous hydrogen chloride. Upon evaporation of the alcohol and excess hydrogen chloride from the solution that results, the ester hydrochloride is obtained [Eq. (2-7)].

$$RCH(NH_3^+)COOH \ + \ R'OH \ (excess) \ \xrightarrow{(H^+)} \ RCH(NH_3^+)COOR' \ + \ H_2O \quad (2\text{-}7)$$

Free amino acid esters are obtained by treatment of the hydrochlorides with an equivalent of base. These are liquids, distillable at reduced pressure, but they are not indefinitely stable. An α-amino ester contains amino and ester functions in the same molecule, and therefore polymerization might be expected by repetition of the amine-ester condensation shown in Eq. (2-8). Polymerization does

occur, to a certain extent, on storage or heating the liquid esters, but the major reaction, especially if the ester is somewhat diluted by a solvent, is formation of a cyclic amide by condensation of only two amino ester molecules [Eq. (2-9)].

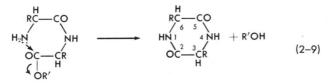

These cyclic amides, rigorously known as 3,6-disubstituted-2,5-dioxopiperazines, are commonly called *diketopiperazines* or amino acid anhydrides.   They are readily formed from many N-(α-aminoacyl)-α-amino acid (dipeptide) derivatives because the two ends of these molecules can, without strain, come into the juxtaposition necessary for coupling.

Although in many respects esters of α-amino acids behave as other aliphatic amines, they are exceptional in forming stable diazo compounds.   Treatment of a primary aliphatic amine with nitrous acid results in the formation of an unstable alkyl diazonium ion.   These normally have only transitory existence and decompose to nitrogen plus a carbonium ion.   The carbonium ion is also unstable, and final products are those derived from it [Eq. (2–10)].

$$\text{R}_2\text{CHCH}_2\text{NH}_2 \xrightarrow{\text{HONO}} [\text{R}_2\text{CHCH}_2\text{N}_2^+] \xrightarrow{-\text{N}_2} [\text{R}_2\text{CHCH}_2^+] \rightarrow$$

$$\text{R}_2\text{C}{=}\text{CH}_2,\ \text{RCH}{=}\text{CHR},\ \text{RCH(OH)CH}_2\text{R, etc.} \qquad (2\text{–}10)$$

In the case of α-amino esters, the diazonium ion can lose a proton to form a resonance-stabilized carbanion, and so diazotization of these substances yields stable diazo compounds [Eq. (2–11)].

$$\text{H}_2\text{NCH}_2\text{COOEt} \xrightarrow{\text{HONO}} [^+\text{N}_2\text{CH}_2\text{COOEt}] \xrightarrow{-\text{H}^+}$$

$$\overset{\displaystyle\text{O}}{\underset{\displaystyle \|}{{}^+\text{N}_2\overset{-}{\text{C}}\text{HCOEt}}} \leftrightarrow \overset{\displaystyle\text{O}^-}{\underset{\displaystyle |}{{}^+\text{N}_2\text{CH}{=}\text{COEt}}} \qquad (2\text{–}11)$$

CYCLIC N-ACYL DERIVATIVES   Because of the proximity of amino and carboxyl functions, a number of N-acyl derivatives of α-amino acids readily form cyclic five-membered-ring derivatives.   Although discussed more fully in other connections, several of these derivatives may be mentioned here.

In an aqueous solution sufficiently alkaline that the amino group is not protonated (so-called Schotten-Baumann conditions), amino acids react with acyl halides and carboxylic acid anhydrides to form N-acyl derivatives [Eq. (2–12)].   Most of these N-acyl compounds,

$$\text{RCOX} + \text{H}_2\text{NCHRCOO}^- \xrightarrow{\text{OH}^-} \text{RCONHCHRCOO}^- + \text{X}^- \qquad (2\text{–}12)$$

if subsequently treated with acetic anhydride and a base such as sodium acetate, undergo cyclodehydration to form substituted 5-

oxazolones. These heterocycles are also known as *azlactones* [Eq. (2–13)]. 5-oxazolones are of interest as synthetic intermediates

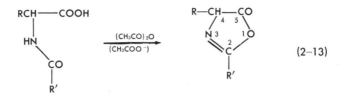

$$(2\text{--}13)$$

(Section 2–4) because, like β-keto esters and β-diketones, they readily form resonance-stabilized anions,

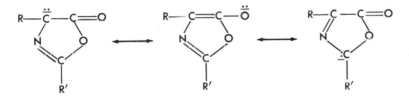

which can condense with aldehydes and ketones. Their formation is also of concern in peptide synthesis because it provides a path for racemization of optically active amino acid derivatives (Section 3–5).

Like other amino compounds, α-amino acids react with isocyanates to form *N*-carbamyl derivatives [Eq. (2–14)]. These substances,

$$R'N{=}C{=}O \;+\; H_2NCHRCOOH \;\rightarrow\; R'NHCONHCHRCOOH \qquad (2\text{--}14)$$

on heating, especially in the presence of acid, cyclize to *hydantoins* (rigorously, 2,4-dioxoimidazolidines). The cyclization occurs not only with *N*-carbamyl-α-amino acids, but also with the corresponding esters and amides [Eq. (2–15)]. Hydantoins are useful synthetic

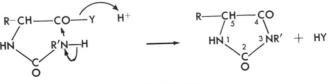

$$Y = OH, OR, NHR$$

intermediates (Section 2–4). *N*-Thiocarbamyl derivatives,

$$R'NHCSNHCHRCOOH$$

formed by reaction of α-amino acid derivatives with isothiocyanates, undergo an analygous cyclization that is the basis of an important method of peptide degradation (Section 4–2).

A third class of cyclic N-acyl derivatives of α-amino acids are the N-carboxy anhydrides, formed by reaction of α-amino acids with phosgene [Eq. (2–16)]. These are the most important intermediates

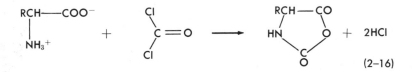

$$(2-16)$$

for preparation of polymers of amino acids (Section 3–8).

METAL COMPLEXES   Functional groups possessing unshared electron pairs, for example, amino groups and carboxylate ions, can act as electron-pair donors in forming coordinate covalent bonds with metal ions. The anions of α-amino acids have two such groups, and these can coordinate simultaneously with the same metal ion, with little distortion of bond angles or distances. Cyclic coordination compounds in which a metal atom is bound to two or more groups derived from a single species are known as *chelate compounds*, and they are most favorably formed when the ring produced has five or six members. Generally, chelate coordination is more favorable than coordination involving similar donor groups from separate donor molecules. One example of chelation by an amino acid is the deep blue substance of empirical formula $(H_2NCH_2COO)_2Cu$, formed by reaction of glycine with cupric ion. This substance is electrically neutral; its solutions do not conduct electricity. It has been shown to possess the structure

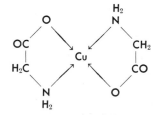

in which the atoms coordinated to the copper ion are disposed around it in a planar arrangement.

An interesting synthetic application of the chelating properties of the α-amino carboxylic acid combination may be seen in the preparation of derivatives of the diamino acid, lysine. Acylating agents do not normally distinguish between the ϵ- and α-amino groups of this substance. However, lysine forms a copper complex in which only the α-amino and carboxyl groups are coordinated with the metal ion. Involvement of the ϵ-amino group is excluded because a sterically unfavorable eight- or nine-membered ring would be formed. Since the normally unshared electron pair of the α-amino nitrogen is used in forming the bond to copper, only the ϵ-amino group is free to react with the acylating agent. After acylation, the copper may be removed by treatment of the complex with hydrogen sulfide. The process is illustrated in Eq. (2–17).

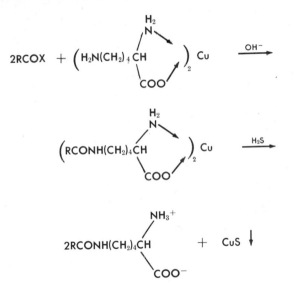

Certain amino acid–cobaltous ion complexes, notably those derived from histidine, are of interest because they share with hemoglobin and only a few other substances the property of reversibly associating with molecular oxygen.

TRANSAMINATION   Primary amines condense with carbonyl compounds, especially with aromatic aldehydes, to form imines [Eq. (2–18)]. When an aromatic aldehyde is involved, the product is

$$RCHO + H_2NR' \rightarrow RCH{=\!=}NR \qquad (2\text{--}18)$$

known as a Schiff base. If a strong base is present, the imine formed from an amine containing α-hydrogen can undergo double-bond migration [Eq. (2–19)]. Since hydrolysis of the new imine (brought

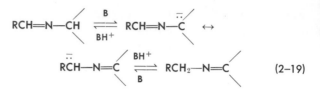

$$(2\text{-}19)$$

about by aqueous acid) yields a new carbonyl compound derived from the amine, plus a new amine derived from the carbonyl compound, the process may be called *transamination*.

When the amine is an α-amino acid, and the carbonyl compound is one bearing strongly electron-withdrawing groups (for example, *p*-nitrobenzaldehyde, or α-dicarbonyl compounds), spontaneous transamination, accompanied by decarboxylation, occurs. The process is analogous to the decarboxylation of β-keto acids [Eqs. (2–20), (2–21)]. It is known as the Strecker degradation.

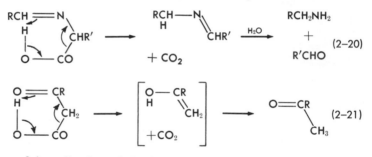

$$(2\text{-}20)$$

$$(2\text{-}21)$$

A useful application of the Strecker degradation lies in the detection and estimation of minute quantities of α-amino acids. When the carbonyl compound involved is *ninhydrin* (1,2,3-triketohydrindene hydrate), an intensely colored substance is produced [Eq. (2–22)]. The quantity of amino acid present may be estimated

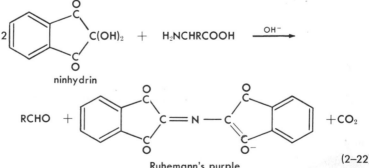

$$(2\text{-}22)$$

colorimetrically or by measurement of the liberated carbon dioxide. As might be expected from Eq. (2–19), ninhydrin, in the presence of base, can deaminate other primary amines bearing α-hydrogen, although not so readily.

Transamination from α-amino acids can be made to occur without decarboxylation, if the base-catalyzed C—N double-bond migration [Eq. (2–19)] can be made to proceed faster than the decarboxylative process [Eq. (2–20)]. Transamination without decarboxylation is important in the metabolism of amino acids. The carbonyl compound utilized in biological transamination is *pyridoxal*. Pyridoxal has been shown to effect in vitro transamination without decarboxylation under the influence of suitable acid-base catalysis.

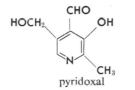

pyridoxal

2–4   Synthesis of α–Amino Acids

Although any of the amino acids that occur in protein can be obtained from protein hydrolysates, it is in many cases more convenient to obtain them by synthesis. Several general methods have been devised for preparing substances with the α-amino carboxylic acid structure. The choice of route usually depends on the availability of starting materials bearing the desired side chains or their precursors.

INTRODUCTION OF THE α-AMINO GROUP   Amino acids can be prepared from α-keto acids by reductive amination [Eq. (2–23)] or re-

$$R—\underset{\underset{O}{\|}}{C}—COOH + NH_3 + 2[H] \rightarrow R—\underset{\underset{NH_3^+}{|}}{CH}—COO^- + H_2O \qquad (2\text{–}23)$$

lated processes, but the most important method of introducing an α-amino group is displacement of α-halogen from α-halo acids by ammonia. This method is best suited for preparation of amino acids possessing hydrocarbon side chains, since the necessary α-chloro or α-bromo acids may readily be obtained by direct halogenation of the corresponding unsubstituted carboxylic acid [*Hell-Volhard-Zelinsky* reaction, Eq. (2–24)].

$$\text{RCH}_2\text{COOH} + \text{X}_2 \xrightarrow{\text{PX}_3} \text{RCHXCOOH} + \text{HX} \qquad (2\text{--}24)$$

Glycine or alanine can be obtained in 50 to 60 per cent yield by treatment of chloroacetic or α-bromopropionic acid with a large excess of ammonia [Eq. (2–25)]. If insufficient ammonia is used,

$$\text{RCHXCOO}^- + \text{NH}_3 \text{ (excess)} \rightarrow \text{RCH(NH}_2)\text{COO}^- + \text{NH}_4^+\text{X}^- \qquad (2\text{--}25)$$

even though it be in excess, formation of secondary [Eq. (2–26)] or

$$\begin{array}{ccc}
\overset{\displaystyle\text{RCHCOO}^-}{\underset{\displaystyle\text{NH}_2^+}{|}} & & \overset{\displaystyle\text{RCHCOO}^-}{\underset{\displaystyle\text{NH}}{|}} \\
\text{+} & + \text{ NH}_3 \rightarrow & | \\
\text{RCHXCOO}^- & & \text{RCHCOO}^-
\end{array} + \text{ NH}_4^+\text{X}^- \qquad (2\text{--}26)$$

tertiary amines is a serious side reaction. With larger α-halo acids, formation of polysubstituted amines is inhibited by the bulk of the side chains, so that the reaction of Eq. (2–26) is less important.

The problem of secondary amine formation may be avoided by use of other ammonia-derived nucleophiles. Chloroacetic acid, for example, reacts with hexamethylenetetramine (the aldehyde-ammonia derived from formaldehyde) to yield a quaternary ammonium derivative that may be acid-hydrolyzed to glycine in an over-all 90 per cent yield [Eq. (2–27)].

$$+ \quad \text{ClCH}_2\text{COOH} \longrightarrow (\text{C}_6\text{H}_{12}\text{N}_4^+)\text{CH}_2\text{COO}^-$$

$$(2\text{--}27)$$

$$\xrightarrow[\text{H}_2\text{O(H}^+)]{} \text{H}_3\text{N}^+\text{CH}_2\text{COO}^- + 6\text{CH}_2\text{O} + 3\text{NH}_3$$

Potassium phthalimide, a common reagent for introduction of an amino group by nucleophilic displacement, is a strong base (that is, phthalimide ion is a strong base), which is merely neutralized by chloroacetic acid. However, if ethyl chloroacetate is used, a displacement process, yielding ethyl phthalimidoacetate, occurs in high yield, and this substance can be quantitatively hydrolyzed to glycine [Eq. (2–28)]. The preparation of primary amines via reaction of an

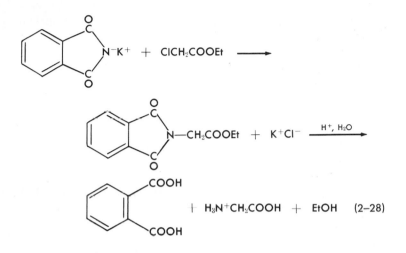

$$+ \; H_3N^+CH_2COOH \; + \; EtOH \quad (2\text{–}28)$$

alkyl halide with potassium phthalimide is known as the *Gabriel synthesis.*

The substitution processes of Eqs. (2–27) and (2–28), exemplified with chloroacetic acid, may be used with other α-halo acids as well.

An early synthesis of peptides was based on the use of α-haloacyl halides. Reaction of an α-haloacyl halide with an amino acid affords an N-(α-haloacyl)-amino acid, which can be ammonolyzed to form a dipeptide [Eq. (2–29)]. This dipeptide can, in turn, be treated with

$$CICHRCOCl + H_2NCHR'COO^- \xrightarrow{\;(OH^-)\;}$$

$$CICHRCONHCHR'COO^- \xrightarrow{\;\text{excess } NH_3\;}$$

$$H_2NCHRCONHCHR'COO^- \quad (2\text{–}29)$$

another haloacyl halide, and so on. Use of optically active α-haloacyl halides leads to optically active peptides, because the displacement of halogen from the α-position by ammonia proceeds with inversion of configuration.

SYNTHESES VIA AMINOMALONIC ESTER   The more versatile general syntheses of α-amino acids begin with derivatives of the simplest member of the series, glycine. One useful intermediate is N-acetyl-aminomalonic ester, conveniently prepared from diethyl malonate.

Diethyl malonate is nitrosated by action of nitrous acid. This reaction, common to enolizable β-dicarbonyl compounds, proceeds by reaction of a resonance-stabilized carbanion with the conjugate acid of nitrous acid [Eq. (2–30)]. Although the nitroso compound is first

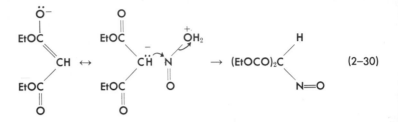

$$(2\text{–}30)$$

formed, it is tautomeric with the more stable oxime [Eq. (2–31)], so

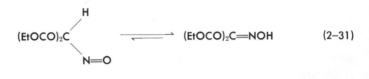

$$(2\text{–}31)$$

that diethyl oximinomalonate is the product obtained. This is hydrogenated over a catalyst to form the amino compound, which is acetylated by action of acetic anhydride [Eq. (2–32)].

$$(EtOCO)_2C{=}NOH \xrightarrow{H_2(Pd)} (EtOCO)_2CHNH_2$$

$$\xrightarrow{(CH_3CO)_2O} (EtOCO)_2CHNHCOCH_3 \qquad (2\text{–}32)$$

Acetylaminomalonic ester retains one acidic α-hydrogen, and can form a resonance-stabilized carbanion, one that readily takes part in nucleophilic displacement or addition reactions [Eq. (2–33)]. The

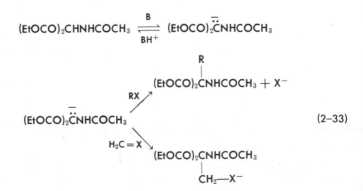

$$(2\text{–}33)$$

fully substituted malonic esters so produced are readily converted to the α-amino acids by acidic hydrolysis. The disubstituted malonic acid that is first formed undergoes decarboxylation under the acidic conditions [Eq. (2–34)].

$$(EtOCO)_2C(R)NHCOCH_3 \xrightarrow{H_3O^+} (HOCO)_2C(R)NHCOCH_3 \xrightarrow{-CO_2}$$

$$HOCOCH(R)NHCOCH_3 \xrightarrow{H_3O^+} HOCOCH(R)NH_3^+ \qquad (2\text{–}34)$$

Figure 2–1 indicates the scope of this general synthesis of α-amino acids. Acetylaminocyanoacetic ester can also be used for synthesis of this type.

SYNTHESES VIA HETEROCYCLIC INTERMEDIATES   The 5-oxazolone obtained by heating glycine with acetic anhydride and sodium acetate (see Section 2–3) can, without isolation, be condensed with alde-hydes and methyl ketones to give 4-alkylideneoxazolones [Eq. (2–35)]. These substances are useful intermediates in the synthesis

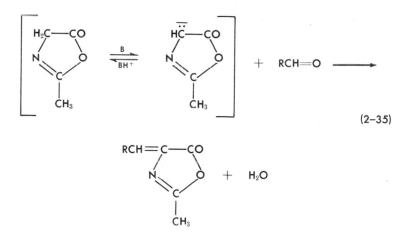

$$(2\text{–}35)$$

of amino acids, keto acids, and related compounds. Alkylidene-oxazolones are hydrolyzed by warming with water to open the azlactone ring (which is much like a cyclic anhydride in its suscepti-bility to hydrolysis), forming N-acyl-α-aminoacrylic acids [Eq. (2–36)]. These may be hydrolyzed under more strenuous conditions to yield α-keto acids [Eq. (2–37)] or first may be reduced (catalytic hydrogenation) and then hydrolyzed to yield α-amino acids [Eq.

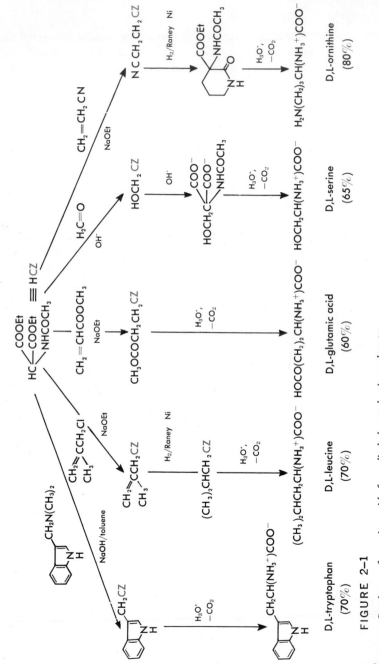

FIGURE 2-1

Syntheses of α-amino acids from diethyl acetylaminomalonate.

22

(2–38)]. Phenylalanine, for example, can thus be synthesized in 70 per cent over-all yield from benzaldehyde.

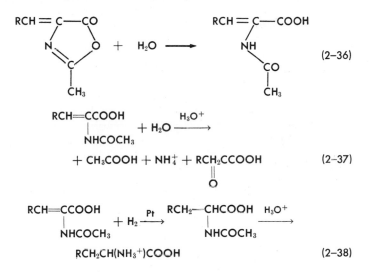

$$RCH = C - CO + H_2O \longrightarrow RCH = C - COOH \quad (2-36)$$

$$RCH = CCOOH + H_2O \xrightarrow{H_3O^+}$$
$$NHCOCH_3$$

$$+ CH_3COOH + NH_4^+ + RCH_2CCOOH \quad (2-37)$$

$$RCH = CCOOH + H_2 \xrightarrow{Pt} RCH_2 - CHCOOH \xrightarrow{H_3O^+}$$
$$NHCOCH_3 \qquad NHCOCH_3$$

$$RCH_2CH(NH_3^+)COOH \quad (2-38)$$

A general synthesis of α-amino acids has recently been developed using 3-phenylhydantoin as the starting point. The CH_2 group in the 5-position of this substance is of an acidity comparable to that of the α-CH_2 group in an aldehyde or ketone. It can be carboxylated by reaction with magnesium methylcarbonate. Reaction (2–39) is

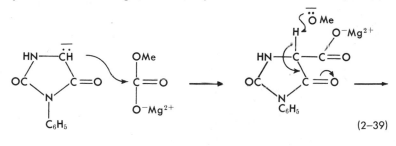

$$(2-39)$$

somewhat similar to the familiar base-catalyzed carbethoxylation of carbonyl compounds by diethyl carbonate [Eq. (2–40)], except that

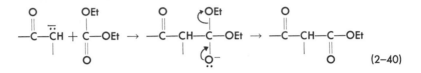

(2–40)

the product is a β-keto acid, obtained in the form of a stable magnesium chelate salt. The magnesium complex formed by the reaction of Eq. (2–39), like the anion of acetylaminomalonic ester, can react with alkyl halides by a nucleophilic displacement process, to produce 5-alkyl derivatives [Eq. (2–41)].

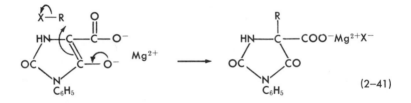

(2–41)

When the alkylation product is acidified, the carboxyl group is converted to the acid form and, being in the position β to another carbonyl group, is lost. The resulting 5-alkyl-3-phenylhydantoin is hydrolyzed, by base, to an amino acid [Eq. (2–42)]. When tri-

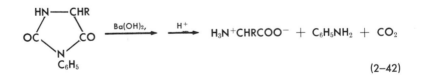

(2–42)

methylene bromide is used as the alkylating agent in this procedure, the nitrogen in position 1 is also alkylated, and on hydrolysis, proline is obtained [Eq. (2–43)].

STRECKER SYNTHESIS   Economical syntheses of α-amino acids are possible if an appropriate aldehyde, bearing one less carbon than the desired product, is available. In the *Strecker synthesis*, an aldehyde is converted to an aminonitrile by action of hydrogen cyanide

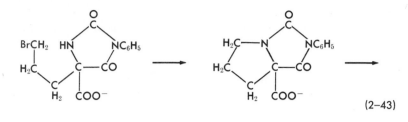

(2–43)

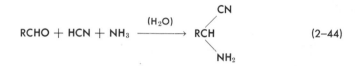

and ammonia [Eq. (2–44)]. The aminonitrile is acid-hydrolyzed to

$$\text{RCHO} + \text{HCN} + \text{NH}_3 \xrightarrow{\text{(H}_2\text{O)}} \underset{\text{NH}_2}{\overset{\text{CN}}{\text{RCH}}} \qquad (2\text{–}44)$$

the amino acid [Eq. (2–45)]. By this route methionine is synthesized

$$\underset{\text{NH}_2}{\overset{\text{CN}}{\text{RCH}}} + \text{H}_2\text{O} \xrightarrow{\text{H}^+} \text{RCH(NH}_3^+)\text{COOH} + \text{NH}_4^+ \qquad (2\text{–}45)$$

in 70 per cent over-all yield from acrolein. The necessary aldehyde is prepared by addition of methyl mercaptan to acrolein [Eq. (2–46)].

$$\text{CH}_3\text{SH} + \text{CH}_2\!\!=\!\!\text{CHCHO} \rightarrow \text{CH}_3\text{SCH}_2\text{CH}_2\text{CHO} \qquad (2\text{–}46)$$

The inconvenience of using hydrogen cyanide as a reagent is avoided, and the yields are frequently improved, by use of the *Bucherer synthesis.* In this process, ammonium carbonate and ammonium cyanide react with the aldehyde to produce a hydantoin. The hydantoin is hydrolyzed to the amino acid. Practical large-scale syntheses of phenylalanine (from phenylacetaldehyde), valine (from isobutyraldehyde), and lysine (from dihydropyran) have been

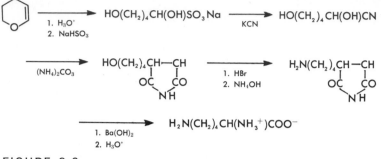

FIGURE 2–2

Synthesis of lysine from dihydropyran; over-all yield is 40 per cent.

based on the Strecker and Bucherer syntheses. The syntheses of lysine is illustrated in Figure 2–2.

2–5 Stereoisomerism of α–Amino Acids

With the exception of glycine and sarcosine, the amino acids listed in Table 2–1 all have four different groups attached to the α-carbon atom. Therefore, they exist as pairs of nonidentical mirror-image isomers or *enantiomorphs*. For all the amino acids isolated from proteins, however, the *configuration* at the asymmetric α-carbon atom, that is, the spatial arrangement of the four different groups around it, is the same, independent of the side chain. This configuration is shown in Figure 2–3. Only a few amino acids from micro-

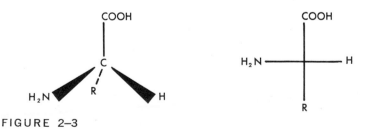

FIGURE 2–3

Configuration at the α-carbon of the common naturally occurring α-amino acids. At the left is a perspective drawing; at the right, the conventional Fischer projection.

biological sources occur with the enantiomorphic (mirror-image) arrangement of groups.

Amino acids with the configuration shown in Figure 2–3 are known as members of the L_s optical series, although the subscript is commonly omitted. This designation arises from the fact that the configurations of the naturally occurring amino acids were, by chemical transformations, shown to be identical to that of the serine isomer that exhibits levorotation in aqueous solution. The opposite configuration defines members of the D series of amino acids.

Several of the common α-amino acids have a second asymmetric center, and so can exist as two chemically different pairs of enantiomorphs. The established configurations of the naturally occurring isomers are shown in Figure 2–4. The non-mirror-image isomers (*diastereomers*) in which only one of the asymmetric centers has been inverted, are indicated by prefixing *allo-* to the trivial name.

Configurations of amino acids relative to each other, and to other optically active molecules such as glyceraldehyde, have been determined by the classic technique of chemical interconversion. In these studies, reactions that do not involve the asymmetric center, or do so with known stereochemical consequences, are used to convert one asymmetric compound into another. One example is the scheme used to demonstrate the relationship between levorotatory serine (the stem of the L series of amino acids) and levorotatory glyceraldehyde (the stem of the L series of carbohydrates), and thus to establish the relationship between the amino acids and the sugars. The

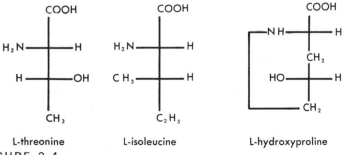

L-threonine   L-isoleucine   L-hydroxyproline

FIGURE 2–4

The naturally-occurring isomers of α-amino acids with two asymmetric centers. Fischer projections.

scheme is shown in Figure 2–5. The two conversions that directly involve the asymmetric carbon atom are nucleophilic displacements carried out under conditions favoring bimolecular reaction kinetics, and thus proceed, on the basis of a large body of evidence, with inversion.

Until 1951, only the relative configurations of asymmetric molecules, established by the sort of interconversions illustrated in Figure 2–5, were known. In that year, a new development in X-ray crystallographic analysis was used to determine the *absolute configuration*, the actual arrangement in terms of left- and right-handedness, of the groups in the sodium rubidium salt of *d*-tartaric acid. Since the optically active tartaric acids had already been related chemically to glyceraldehyde, and glyceraldehyde to the α-amino acids, the absolute configuration of all the amino acids became known. An independent X-ray analysis of the D-isoleucine structure later confirmed the assignments and the chemical interrelationships that led to them.

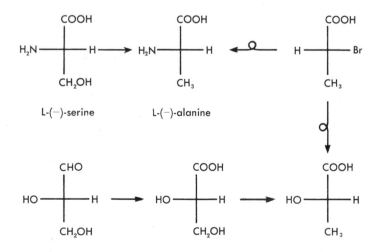

FIGURE 2–5

The relation between the configuration of (−)-serine and that of (−)-glyceraldehyde. Fischer projections are used. Looped arrows indicate reactions that occur with inversion at the asymmetric center.

RESOLUTION OF RACEMIC MIXTURES OF AMINO ACIDS   Chemical synthesis of amino acids (or anything else) from optically inactive reagents results in optically inactive equimolar mixtures of enantiomorphs. For most biological and chemical purposes, such *racemic mixtures* must be resolved, that is, separated into their two optically active components.

The most common method of chemical resolution uses formation of diastereomeric salts, and this technique is readily applicable to amino acids, which have built in salt-forming functions. The synthetic mixture of enantiomorphs is allowed to react with an optically active acid or base, in a solvent and at concentrations so chosen that one of the two different salts formed [Eq. (2–47)] precipitates from

$$\text{D,L-RCONHCHRCOOH} + d\text{-B} \nearrow \begin{array}{l} (\text{D-RCONHCHRCOO}^-, d\text{-BH}^+) \\[1em] \searrow (\text{L-RCONHCHRCOO}^-, d\text{-BH}^+) \end{array} \qquad (2\text{–}47)$$

solution. That salt obtained in greater purity, which may be either the more-soluble or less-soluble one, is isolated and decomposed to yield active amino acid. With monoamino-monocarboxylic acids, this process is usually carried out using N-acylated derivatives and optically active bases. Because they are readily hydrolyzed by dilute acid, so that the amino acid itself may readily be recovered, N-formyl derivatives of amino acids (Section 3–1) are often used. Suitable resolving agents are alkaloids such as brucine and strychnine, or a previously resolved synthetic base such as 1-phenylethylamine.

Amino acids with basic side chains, such as lysine and histidine, may be resolved without acylation, through salt formation with optically active acids. Reagents for this purpose include optically active isomers of camphoric and camphorsulfonic acids.

Enzymes that catalyze the hydrolysis of amino acid derivatives (see Section 5–4) are generally absolutely specific in terms of the optical activity of those derivatives. They will catalyze reactions of one enantiomer, but not the other; this specificity arises from the fact that the enzymes themselves are complex, highly asymmetric molecules, and it can be used to effect resolution of racemic amino acid mixtures.

The most thoroughly worked out enzymatic resolution of amino acids uses the action of renal acylases, hydrolytic enzymes derived from mammalian kidney. These enzymes catalyze the hydrolysis of N-acetyl- or N-chloroacetyl-L-amino acids, without affecting the D-isomer. Their action on a mixture of D- and L-N-acylamino acids results in a mixture of L-amino acid and D-acylamino acid; this mixture can easily be separated and both isomers can be recovered in high purity [Eq. (2–48)].

$$\text{D,L-ClCH}_2\text{CONHCHRCOOH} \xrightarrow{\text{H}_2\text{O} + \text{renal acylase}}$$

$$\text{D-ClCH}_2\text{CONHCHRCOOH} + \text{L-RCH(NH}_3^+)\text{COO}^- + \text{ClCH}_2\text{COOH} \qquad (2\text{–}48)$$

The optical purity of an amino acid can, of course, be determined by measurement of the degree to which it rotates the plane of polarization of a beam of plane-polarized monochromatic light, if the rotation of the pure optically active material is already known. A more precise method of determining optical purity, however, uses the virtually absolute optical specificity of enzymes. The amount of oxygen consumed, for example, upon treatment of an alleged L-amino acid with an enzyme system that oxidatively deaminates amino acids of the D optical series is a measure of the amount of D-enantiomer present in the sample [Eq. (2–49)].

$$\text{D,L-H}_3\overset{+}{\text{N}}\text{CHRCOO}^- + \text{O}_2 + \text{H}_2\text{O} \xrightarrow{\text{D-amino acid oxidase}}$$

$$\text{RCOCOOH} + \text{L-H}_3\overset{+}{\text{N}}\text{CHRCOO}^- + \text{NH}_3 + \text{H}_2\text{O}_2 \qquad (2\text{–}49)$$

References

Reviews

   L. A. Cohen and B. Witkop, "Rearrangements in the Chemistry of Amino Acids and Peptides," in P. deMayo (ed.), *Molecular Rearrangements,* Part 2, Wiley (Interscience), New York, 1964, pp. 965–1017.
   J. P. Greenstein and M. Winitz, *Chemistry of the Amino Acids,* (3 vols.), Wiley, New York, 1961. Volume 1 concerns the properties and synthesis of α-amino acids in general; volume 3 contains lengthy discussions of the individual amino acids.
   G. R. Tristram and R. H. Smith, "The Amino Acid Composition of Some Purified Proteins," *Advan. Protein Chem.,* **18,** 227–318 (1963).

B. Tschierisch and K. Mothes, "Amino Acids: Structure and Distribution," in M. Florkin and H. S. Mason (eds.), *Comparative Biochemistry,* Vol. V, Academic Press, New York, 1963, pp. 1–90.

Paper

H. L. Finkbeiner, "A Generic Synthesis of Amino Acids by the Carboxylation of 3-Phenylhydantoin," *J. Am. Chem. Soc.,* **86,** 961–962 (1964).

3

▪ PEPTIDE SYNTHESIS

FOR A NUMBER of reasons, research activity in peptide synthesis has become intense. Synthetic peptides themselves are of interest as biologically active substances, as test materials for probing details of biochemical processes, and as models with which to study the chemical and physical properties of proteins. In addition, rational total synthesis of peptides has been necessary to confirm some of the structures deduced for naturally occurring peptides and fragments of proteins. Finally, and not unimportantly, rational peptide synthesis represents chemical mountain climbing of a high order. The largest molecules the chemist has so far prepared in pure, homogeneous form are peptides, and their synthesis has not been made any easier by the polyfunctionality of the components from which they are constructed.

In the laboratory, as in nature, peptide synthesis generally begins with amino acids. These may be converted to polymers in an undirected fashion (see Section 3–8), or condensed in a stepwise manner to form specific molecular species. Since amino acids are di- or polyfunctional molecules, directed coupling of the carboxyl group of one with the amino group of another is achieved only by protecting some of the functional groups. This is usually accomplished by

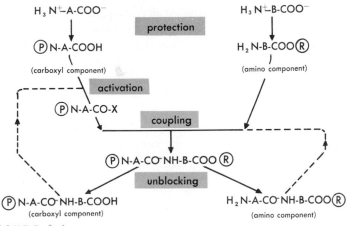

FIGURE 3–1

Generalized peptide synthesis. The symbols **A** *and* **B** *represent the α-carbon atoms and side chains of amino acids.* **P** *and* **R** *are amino- and carboxyl-protecting groups, respectively.*

temporary attachment of *blocking groups* that inhibit the reactivity of the functions to be protected. Blocking groups that are readily introduced and readily and selectively removed must be employed. After these protecting groups are introduced, one of the components of the peptide-bond-to-be, usually that providing the carboxyl side, is converted to a reactive form. The so activated carboxyl component and the amino component are then allowed to react to form the peptide; finally, blocking groups are removed. The general scheme is indicated in Figure 3–1; individual steps are discussed in subsequent sections.

In recent years many protecting, activating, and coupling procedures have been devised. We shall consider methods that have proved consistently useful in the synthesis of higher peptides.

3–1 Protection of Amino Groups

For directed peptide coupling, the α-amino group of the carboxyl component must be prevented from reacting with the activated carboxyl group. This is accomplished by introducing substituents that reduce the normal nucleophilicity of the amine, usually by reducing the availability of its unshared electron pair. Acylation of an amine provides effective protection, but common acyl groups, for example, acetyl or benzoyl, will not serve. An N-acetyl or N-benzoyl group cannot later be removed without at the same time rupturing the peptide bonds one is concerned with forming. The most useful protecting groups have been alkoxycarbonyl substituents.

THE BENZYLOXYCARBONYL GROUP   In 1932, Max Bergmann and Leonidas Zervas introduced the benzyloxycarbonyl (or carbobenzyloxy) protective group. This invention made modern peptide synthesis possible, and benzyloxycarbonyl is still the first choice for protection of amino nitrogen in peptide synthesis. Benzyloxycarbonyl chloride is prepared by reaction of phosgene with benzyl alcohol [Eq. (3–1)]. This acid chloride reacts with amines or amino

$$C_6H_5CH_2OH + Cl\!-\!CO\!-\!Cl \;\rightarrow\; C_6H_5CH_2O\!-\!CO\!-\!Cl + HCl \quad (3\text{--}1)$$

acids to form the corresponding urethanes, N-benzyloxycarbonyl derivatives, in high yield [Eq. (3–2)]. N-Benzyloxycarbonyl deriva-

$$\underset{\overset{\|}{O}}{C_6H_5CH_2O\overset{}{C}}\!-\!Cl + H_2NR + OH^- \;\rightarrow\; \underset{\overset{\|}{O}}{C_6H_5CH_2O\overset{}{C}}\!-\!NHR + Cl^- \quad (3\text{--}2)$$

tives, like other amides, do not readily react with activated carboxyl groups, but unlike other amides, they may be converted to the original amino compound under nonhydrolytic conditions.

The benzyl-ester link of an N-benzyloxycarbonyl group is stable to the relatively mild alkaline conditions that saponify peptide methyl or ethyl esters, but it does undergo acid-catalyzed alkyl-oxygen fission. Acid cleavage is facilitated by the presence of a nucleophilic reagent that may attack the benzylic carbon atom. Practical removal of an N-benzyloxycarbonyl group is brought about by treatment with 2 N hydrogen bromide in an organic solvent (acetic acid, nitromethane, trifluoroacetic acid) at room temperature [Eq. (3–3)]. Complete cleavage requires only minutes.

$$C_6H_5CH_2\!-\!\overset{\overset{\displaystyle H^+}{O}}{\underset{:Br^-}{O\overset{\|}{C}}}\!-\!NHR \;\rightarrow\; C_6H_5CH_2Br + \left[O\!=\!\underset{\overset{|}{OH}}{C}\!-\!NHR \right] \quad (3\text{--}3)$$

Once the benzyl-oxygen bond has been broken, the nitrogen atom is still involved in a carbamic acid structure. Carbamic acids, however, have only a transitory existence in acid solution; they immediately decarboxylate to form carbon dioxide and an ammonium salt [Eq. (3–4)]. The ammonium salt may be precipitated by addition

$$\left[\begin{matrix} \text{OH} \\ | \\ \text{O}\!=\!\text{C}\!-\!\text{NHR} \end{matrix} \right] \rightarrow \text{O}\!=\!\text{C}\!=\!\text{O} + \text{H}_2\text{NR} \xrightarrow{\text{H}^+} \text{H}_3\text{N}^+\text{R} \qquad (3\text{–}4)$$

of ether. Peptide bonds and most of the functional groups of amino acids are stable to these conditions, although not all other protecting groups will survive them.

An alternative method for removing benzyloxycarbonyl groups utilizes a different peculiarity of benzyl ethers and esters. Benzyl-oxygen cleavage may be brought about reductively, with the formation of toluene. The process is known as *hydrogenolysis* [Eq. (3–5)].

$$\text{C}_6\text{H}_5\text{CH}_2\!-\!\text{O}\!-\!\overset{\overset{\text{O}}{\|}}{\text{C}}\!-\!\text{NHR} + 2[\text{H}] \rightarrow \text{C}_6\text{H}_5\text{CH}_3 + \left[\text{HO}\!-\!\overset{\overset{\text{O}}{\|}}{\text{C}}\!-\!\text{NHR} \right] \quad (3\text{–}5)$$

Hydrogenolysis of a benzyloxycarbonyl derivative is most conveniently carried out by bubbling hydrogen through a suspension of a palladium catalyst in a solution of the derivative. Palladium, rather than platinum, is used because palladium catalysts have less tendency to effect hydrogenation of aromatic rings. If poisoning of the catalyst makes this method impractical when the sulfur-containing amino acids (cysteine and methionine) are present, hydrogenolysis may be brought about by treatment with sodium in liquid ammonia.

In the benzyloxycarbonyl group the chemist has a blocking group that is readily introduced to amino acids (or their esters) and is removable from peptides under conditions that are not harmful to peptide bonds. The success of this protecting group has led to development of a number of modified versions. *p*-Nitrobenzyloxycarbonyl substitution yields substances that are more readily crystallized than benzyloxycarbonyl derivatives themselves. The *p*-nitrobenzyloxycarbonyl group is less readily cleaved by hydrogen bromide solutions. In contrast, *p*-methoxybenzyloxycarbonyl groups are removed at 0° by anhydrous trifluoroacetic acid, a set of conditions to which the unsubstituted benzyloxycarbonyl group is stable. Azo-substituted benzyloxycarbonyl groups have also been used; these give colored derivatives, which are easily detected during chromatography.

THE *t*-BUTOXYCARBONYL GROUP   A second alkoxycarbonyl blocking group, which, when used with the benzyloxycarbonyl, can provide differential protection of functional groups, is the *t*-butoxycarbonyl. This group may, like the benzyloxycarbonyl group, be removed by acid-catalyzed cleavage of an alkyl-oxygen bond, but conditions that do not affect a benzyl-oxygen link can be used. The *t*-butoxycarbonyl group is removed in an hour or less at 20°C, upon treatment with anhydrous trifluoroacetic acid or 2 *N* hydrochloric acid [Eq. (3–6)]. The *t*-butoxycarbonyl group is unaffected by

$$(CH_3)_3C-O-CONHR \xrightarrow{H^+} \left[(CH_3)_3C^+ \right] + \left[HO-CONHR \right]$$

$$\xrightarrow{H^+} (CH_3)_2C{=}CH_2 + CO_2 + H_3N^+R \quad (3{-}6)$$

hydrogenation, and, like all tertiary esters, is extremely resistant to hydrolysis by base.

Thus, in the same molecule, groups protected by a *t*-butoxycarbonyl group may be unblocked without releasing those protected by a benzyloxycarbonyl group; this is brought about by mild acid treatment. The opposite result, unblocking groups protected by benzyloxycarbonyl while leaving protected those covered by *t*-butoxycarbonyl, is achieved by hydrogenation. This sort of versatility is much sought after in any complex synthesis.

A *t*-butoxycarbonyl group cannot be introduced through the corresponding acid chloride, since this is much too unstable [Eq. (3–7)], but the acid azide may be used [Eq. (3–8)]. The azide reacts

$$\begin{array}{c} O \\ \parallel \\ (CH_3)_3COC-Cl \underset{\geq 10°}{\longrightarrow} (CH_3)_2C{=}CH_2 + HCl + CO_2 \end{array} \quad (3{-}7)$$

$$\begin{array}{c} O \\ \parallel \\ (CH_3)_3COC-N_3 + H_2NR \end{array} \rightarrow \begin{array}{c} O \\ \parallel \\ (CH_3)_3COC-NHR + HN_3 \end{array} \quad (3{-}8)$$

with amines or amino acids in aqueous or organic solvents, in the presence of a weak base. (See Section 3–4 for further discussion of acyl azides.)

t-Butoxycarbonyl hydrazide, a stable source of the necessary azide, is prepared in a two-step sequence [Eqs. (3–9), (3–10)]. It is converted to the reactive azide by treatment with nitrous acid [Eq. (3–11)].

$$(CH_3)_3C—OH + Cl—\overset{\overset{O}{\|}}{C}—S—C_6H_5 \xrightarrow{\text{pyridine}} (CH_3)_3C—O—\overset{\overset{O}{\|}}{C}—S—C_6H_5 \quad (3\text{–}9)$$

$$(CH_3)_3C—O—\overset{\overset{O}{\|}}{C}—S—C_6H_5 + NH_2NH_2 \rightarrow$$

$$(CH_3)_3C—O—\overset{\overset{O}{\|}}{C}—NHNH_2 + C_6H_5SH \quad (3\text{–}10)$$

$$(CH_3)_3C—O—\overset{\overset{O}{\|}}{C}—NHNH_2 + HONO \rightarrow (CH_3)_3C—O—\overset{\overset{O}{\|}}{C}—N_3 \quad (3\text{–}11)$$

THE TOLUENESULFONYL GROUP   Reaction between an amine and p-toluenesulfonyl chloride in the presence of base yields the toluenesulfonamide [Eq. (3–12)]. Toluenesulfonamides do not react with

$$CH_3C_6H_5SO_2—Cl + H_2NR + OH^- \rightarrow CH_3C_6H_5SO_2—NHR + Cl^- + H_2O$$
$$(3\text{–}12)$$

acylating agents and are stable to almost all the conditions that may be encountered in peptide synthesis. They are cleaved by treatment with sodium in liquid ammonia, which effects a reductive scission of the S—N bond [Eq. (3–13)].

$$CH_3C_6H_5SO_2—NHR + 2[H] \xrightarrow{(Na/NH_3)} CH_3C_6H_5SO_2^-Na^+ + H_2NR \quad (3\text{–}13)$$

THE TRITYL GROUP   Triphenylmethyl chloride (trityl chloride) reacts with amino acid esters in organic solvents, in the presence of base, to form N-triphenylmethyl- (N-trityl-) amino acid esters [Eq. (3–14)]. Although these derivatives are still somewhat basic,

$$(C_6H_5)_3C—Cl + H_2NR \rightarrow (C_6H_5)_3C—NHR + Cl^- + H^+ \quad (3\text{–}14)$$

they are sterically prevented from reaction with activated carboxyl derivatives. N-trityl-α-amino acid methyl (or ethyl) esters may be saponified to produce the N-trityl-amino acids, but saponification is often sluggish because the bulky trityl substituent interferes with reactions at the carboxyl group as well as at the amino group. This steric effect is a disadvantage in the use of activated N-trityl-α-amino acids as carboxyl components in peptide coupling; however, the trityl residue may sometimes be used to advantage in protection of groups other than α-amino.

The trityl group is not removed by alkali, but because of the stability of the resulting triphenylmethyl cation, an intermediate in the acid-catalyzed reaction, it is extremely labile to dilute acids, and is removed by heating for a few minutes with dilute aqueous acetic acid [Eq. (3–15)].

$$(C_6H_5)_3C{-}NHR + H^+ \rightarrow [(C_6H_5)_3C^+] + H_2NR \xrightarrow{H_2O} (C_6H_5)_3C{-}OH$$

$$(3\text{–}15)$$

OTHER N-PROTECTING GROUPS   In addition to the four groups described above, many others have occasionally been used in peptide synthesis or for protection of amino groups in other syntheses. Three may be mentioned. Amines and amino acids may be converted to N-formyl derivatives by use of a mixture of formic acid and acetic anhydride. Reaction probably proceeds through the mixed formic-acetic anhydride [Eqs. (3–16), (3–17)]. The formyl

$$(CH_3CO)_2O + HCOOH \rightleftharpoons CH_3\overset{\overset{\text{O}}{\|}}{C}{-}O{-}\overset{\overset{\text{O}}{\|}}{C}H + CH_3COOH \quad (3\text{–}16)$$

$$CH_3\overset{\overset{\text{O}}{\|}}{C}{-}O{-}\overset{\overset{\text{O}}{\|}}{C}H + H_2NR \rightarrow CH_3COOH + H\overset{\overset{\text{O}}{\|}}{C}NHR \quad (3\text{–}17)$$

group is readily removed by treatment with N hydrochloric acid in methanol at room temperature.

Reaction of an amine with trifluoroacetic anhydride or ethyl trifluorothiolacetate [Eq. (3–18)] results in formation of the N-

$$CF_3\overset{\overset{\text{O}}{\|}}{C}{-}SEt + H_2NR \rightarrow CF_3\overset{\overset{\text{O}}{\|}}{C}{-}NHR + EtSH \quad (3\text{–}18)$$

trifluoroacetyl derivative. Trifluoroacetamides are among the few amides that are readily hydrolyzed by base. N sodium hydroxide at room temperature suffices.

Amino acids can be converted to N-phthaloyl derivatives by fusion with phthalic anhydride [Eq. (3-19)]. There is danger that racemiza-

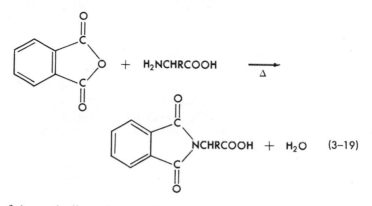

$$(3-19)$$

tion of the optically active α-carbon atom may occur in this process, and other, milder methods of introducing the phthaloyl protecting group have been devised. In contrast to other N-acyl-α-amino acids, the N-phthaloyl derivatives can be converted to stable acid chlorides that can be used as activated carboxyl components in peptide coupling. A set of conditions for removal of the phthaloyl blocking group without affecting peptide bonds involves treatment with hydrazine [Eq. (3-20)]; unfortunately this can result in undesired

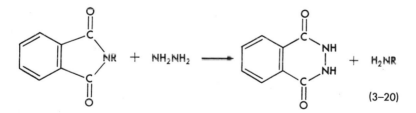

$$(3-20)$$

hydrazinolysis (that is, hydrazide formation) of ester groups that may be present.

3-2   Protection of Carboxyl Functions

Peptide coupling can be carried out successfully without protection of the carboxyl group of the amino component only if the activation and coupling steps are not combined. If the two steps are combined in one operation, the carboxyl groups of both components will compete for the activating agent and a mixture of coupled products will result.

Ester formation is the most common form of carboxyl protection. Methyl and ethyl esterification of amino acids has been discussed in Section 2–3. When desired, these groups are removed by saponification, using aqueous alkali-organic solvent mixtures (for example, water-dioxane or water-pyridine) at room temperature. Cleavage usually requires only minutes to hours. However, rupture of peptide bonds can occur in some cases, and yields are not always satisfactory.

Methyl or ethyl esters are used as carboxyl-protecting groups when it is desired eventually to convert the carboxyl end of the peptide to an acyl azide (Section 3–4).

Benzyl esters, which are converted to the free carboxylic acids by the same treatments that remove *N*-benzyloxycarbonyl groups, are generally formed by azeotropic distillation of water from a mixture of benzyl alcohol and the amino acid in the presence of an acid catalyst such as benzene- or toluenesulfonic acid.

p-Nitrobenzyl esters may be prepared by a direct esterification using *p*-nitrobenzyl alcohol under acidic conditions, but are also conveniently prepared by reaction of *p*-nitrobenzyl bromide with the silver salt of an *N*-protected amino acid [Eq. (3–21)]. Selective

$$\text{RCOO}^-\text{Ag}^+ + \text{Br}\!-\!\text{CH}_2\!\!\left\langle\!\!\bigcirc\!\!\right\rangle\!\!\text{NO}_2 \;\rightarrow\; \text{RCOO}\!-\!\text{CH}_2\!\!\left\langle\!\!\bigcirc\!\!\right\rangle\!\!\text{NO}_2 + \text{AgBr}$$

$$(3\text{--}21)$$

removal of *N*-benzyloxcarbonyl groups from peptide or amino acid nitrobenzyl esters is brought about by treatment with hydrogen bromide in acetic acid (see Section 3–1) [Eq. (3–22)].

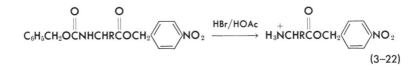

$$(3\text{--}22)$$

t-Butyl esters are not hydrolyzed by alkali or attacked by other nucleophilic reagents, but they can be removed when necessary by the same reagents that remove *t*-butoxycarbonyl groups. The *t*-butyl ester function is introduced by direct esterification of an amino acid or an *N*-acylamino acid. Isobutylene and a sulfuric acid catalyst, using methylene chloride as a solvent, serve the purpose [Eq. (3–23)]. A transesterification reaction with *t*-butyl acetate can

$$RCOOH + (CH_3)_2C{=}CH_2 \xrightarrow{(H^+)} \overset{\overset{\textstyle O}{\|}}{R}COC(CH_3)_3 \qquad (3\text{--}23)$$

also be used [Eq. (3–24)].

$$\overset{\overset{\textstyle O}{\|}}{R}COOH + CH_3COC(CH_3)_3 \underset{}{\overset{(H^+)}{\rightleftharpoons}} \overset{\overset{\textstyle O}{\|}}{R}COC(CH_3)_3 + CH_3COOH \qquad (3\text{--}24)$$

3–3 Protection of Side-Chain Functions

AMINO GROUPS   If a lysine residue is to be the last group at the amino end of a peptide chain, so that the protecting groups necessary for both its α- and ϵ-amino groups may be simultaneously removed, the blocking groups on the two nitrogens may be identical. If lysine is to be present inside the peptide to be synthesized, differential protection of the two amino groups is required.

Acyl blocking groups, such as benzyloxycarbonyl or *t*-butoxycarbonyl, may be selectively attached to the ϵ-amino group of lysine by reaction of the acylating agent with the copper chelate of the amino acid (Section 2–3). Once the metal ion is removed, the α-amino group may be protected with a different reagent. The alternative approach, acylation first of the α-nitrogen, can also be used. Lysine reacts with benzaldehyde to form an ϵ-benzylidene derivative [Eq. (3–25)]. The benzylidene protecting group is not itself of gen-

$$C_6H_5CHO + H_2N(CH_2)_4\underset{\underset{\textstyle NH_3^+}{|}}{C}HCOO^- \rightarrow C_6H_5CH{=}N(CH_2)_4\underset{\underset{\textstyle NH_3^+}{|}}{C}HCOO^- \qquad (3\text{--}25)$$

eral utility in peptide synthesis, although the benzalazine structure $(C_6H_5CH{=}N{-})$ is stable to alkaline hydrolysis. However, a benzyloxycarbonyl group may be attached to the α-amino group by reaction of the ϵ-protected amino acid with benzyloxycarbonyl chloride in aqueous base. After this step, the benzylidene group on the ϵ-amino function is removed by treatment with aqueous acid [Eq. (3–26)]. N-α-carbobenzyloxylysine can thus be prepared in 60 per cent over-all yield.

$$C_6H_5CH{=}N(CH_2)_4CHCOOH \xrightarrow{\;H_2O,\,(H^+)\;} \overset{+}{H_3}N(CH_2)_4CHCOOH + C_6H_5CHO$$

with NHZ below on both sides.

$$(Z = C_6H_5CH_2OCO{-})$$

$$(3\text{--}26)$$

CARBOXYL GROUPS   Differential protection of the two carboxyl groups of glutamic and aspartic acids is necessary if these residues are to be incorporated into peptides.

Acid-catalyzed direct esterification of aspartic or glutamic acid by methyl, ethyl, or benzyl alcohols can be made to yield the diesters. If the esterification is not driven to completion, only the side-chain esters are obtained [Eq. (3–27)]. Acid-catalyzed esterification, which

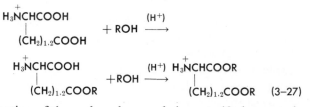

$$(3\text{--}27)$$

requires protonation of the carboxyl group being esterified, proceeds most rapidly at the carboxyl farther from the positive charge already carried by the α-amino group.

Protection of side-chain carboxyl groups as methyl or ethyl esters is not desirable. Rearrangements are apt to occur during the alkaline hydrolysis required to regenerate the free carboxyl group. These rearrangements, which proceed through cyclic intermediates, result in converting peptides involving the α-carboxyl to products in which the side-chain carboxyl is part of the peptide backbone [Eq. (3–28)].

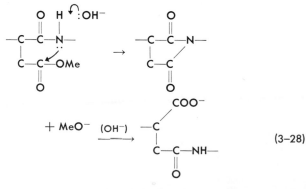

$$(3\text{--}28)$$

Glutamic and aspartic acid α-benzyl esters are prepared from the corresponding dibenzyl esters by carefully controlled cleavage, using hydrogen iodide in acetic acid. Acid cleavage of benzyl esters, which requires protonation of the ester oxygen [cf. Eq. (3–3)], occurs faster at the site more removed from the ammonium ion. The half-benzyl esters of aspartic and glutamic acids can be converted to benzyl-t-butyl esters by treatment with isobutylene and acid catalyst. These may then be converted to the corresponding half-t-butyl esters by saponification or hydrogenolysis [Eq. (3–29)].

$$\overset{+}{\underset{|}{H_3NCHCOOCH_2C_6H_5}} \quad \overset{+}{\underset{|}{H_3NCHCOOCH_2C_6H_5}}$$
$$(CH_2)_{1.2}COOH \quad \rightarrow \quad (CH_2)_{1.2}COOC(CH_3)_3 \quad \rightarrow$$

$$\overset{+}{\underset{|}{H_3NCHCOOH}}$$
$$(CH_2)_{1.2}COOC(CH_3)_3 \qquad (3\text{–}29)$$

SULFHYDRYL GROUPS   The sulfhydryl group of cysteine must be protected at all times during peptide synthesis. Some mercaptide ion is present whenever there is an unprotected mercapto group. (The pK_A of an aliphatic thiol is about 10.) Mercaptide ion is a powerful nucleophile capable of successful competition, even at low concentrations, for reaction with activated carboxyl groups. More important, however, is the fact that mercaptans, *via* the mercaptide ions, are readily oxidized by air or other reagents to form disulfides [Eq. (3–30)].

$$2RSH + [O] \rightarrow RS\text{—}SR + H_2O \qquad (3\text{–}30)$$

Cysteine is most commonly handled in peptide synthesis as S-benzyl cysteine, prepared by treatment of cysteine, in the form of a sodium salt in liquid ammonia, with benzyl chloride [Eq. (3–31)].

$$\underset{|}{H_2NCHCOO^-} + C_6H_5CH_2Cl \xrightarrow{NH_3(l)} \underset{|}{H_2NCHCOO^-} \qquad (3\text{–}31)$$
$$CH_2S^- \qquad\qquad\qquad\qquad\qquad CH_2SCH_2C_6H_5$$

When it is desired to remove the protecting group, hydrogenolysis by sodium in liquid ammonia is used. Because this treatment frequently results in low yields when applied to large peptides, S-benzyloxycarbonyl and S-trityl groups have occasionally been substituted for S-benzyl.

GUANIDINE GROUPS   The guanidine function of the arginine

side chain is an extremely strong base with pK_A about 13. Its cation is resonance-stabilized:

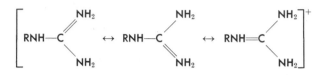

Throughout most of the manipulations of peptide synthesis in which this basicity might interfere, a guanidine group can be protected by protonation; it will remain protonated in media sufficiently basic to maintain α-amino groups in their acylable, free base form. However, protonated arginine derivatives are often highly water-soluble materials, difficult to crystallize and purify.

More satisfactory protection of the arginine side chain is obtained by nitration of the amino acid with a mixture of concentrated nitric and fuming sulfuric acids [Eq. (3–32)]. The nitro group so attached depresses the basic character of the guanidine group. It is removed, when so desired, by catalytic reduction [Eq. (3–33)].

$$(H_2N)_2^+CNH(CH_2)_3CH(\overset{+}{N}H_3)COOH + HNO_3 \xrightarrow{(H_2SO_4)}$$

$$O_2N\text{—}NHC(\text{=}NH)NH(CH_2)_3\overset{+}{C}H(NH_3)COOH \qquad (3\text{–}32)$$

$$O_2N\text{—}NH\text{—}\underset{\underset{NH}{\|}}{C}\text{—}NHR + H_2 \xrightarrow[(H^+)]{Pd} NH_3 + (H_2N)_2^+C\text{—}NHR \qquad (3\text{–}33)$$

OTHER GROUPS   The phenolic hydroxyl of tyrosine and the alcoholic hydroxyl of serine or threonine do not normally require protection in peptide synthesis. They can, however, be protected as acetyl derivatives or benzyl ethers. O-Acetyl serine is prepared by saturating a suspension of serine in glacial acetic acid with hydrogen chloride, an inversion of the preparation of α-amino acid carboxyl esters (Section 2–3).

The imidazole group of the histidine side chain can occasionally be left unprotected during peptide synthesis, although it is generally more satisfactory to plan synthesis involving histidine around N_{im}-benzyl-histidine, which is prepared by treatment of a sodium derivative of histidine, in liquid ammonia, with benzyl chloride [Eq. (3–34)].

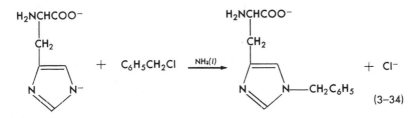

(3–34)

The N-benzyl group can be removed by hydrogenolysis.

3–4   Activation and Coupling Procedures

Mixing an aliphatic amine with a carboxylic acid at room temperature results only in formation of a salt. To convert this salt into an amide [Eq. (3–35)] requires temperatures too high for survival of

$$\text{RCOOH} + \text{H}_2\text{NR}' \;\rightleftharpoons\; \text{RCOO}^- \;\; \text{H}_3\text{N}^+\text{R}' \;\xrightarrow{\Delta}\; \text{RCONHR}' + \text{H}_2\text{O}$$

(3–35)

most peptides. Therefore, formation of a peptide bond is generally carried out after conversion of the carboxyl component to a more reactive acyl derivative, one which reacts with the amino component under mild conditions.

The detailed mechanism of reaction between amines and acyl derivatives depends on the nature of the amine and the group, originally attached to the acyl group, that leaves when the amide is formed. With the reactants normally encountered in peptide coupling, initial nucleophilic attack by the amine leads to an intermediate species that may revert to starting materials or decompose to products, as indicated in Eq. (3–36). The more electronegative is the *leaving group* —X (that is, the less basic X or more acidic X—H), the more rapid and thermodynamically favorable is amide formation likely to be. The over-all reaction proceeds relatively slowly if X— is an alkoxyl group, as in an ester, and rapidly if X— is halide, as in an acid chloride. Although Eq. (3–36) consists of two successive

$$R\!-\!\overset{\overset{\displaystyle O}{\|}}{C}\!-\!X \;\rightleftharpoons\; \left[\; R\!-\!\overset{\overset{\displaystyle OH}{|}}{\underset{\underset{\displaystyle R'\!-\!NH}{|}}{C}}\!-\!X \;\right] \;\rightleftharpoons\; R\!-\!\overset{\overset{\displaystyle O}{\|}}{\underset{\underset{\displaystyle R'\!-\!NH}{|}}{C}} \;+\; X^- + H^+ \qquad (3\text{–}36)$$

equilibrium steps, the reactions proceeding to the right are so highly favored under the conditions used that amide formation is essentially irreversible.

Amide formation via acid chlorides was used for early peptide syntheses: An N-protected carboxyl component was converted to its acid chloride by treatment with thionyl chloride or phosphorus pentachloride, and this activated derivative was allowed to react with the amino component. The forms of amino nitrogen protection that can be used with this method are limited, however; in general N-acyl-α-aminoacyl halides do not retain the optical activity of the α-carbon asymmetric center (Section 3–5). Optically stable N-benzyloxycarbonylamino acid chlorides can be prepared at low temperature, but at room temperature they undergo decomposition to amino acid N-carboxy anhydrides (Section 3–8) and are therefore inconvenient to use.

Four carboxyl activation and coupling procedures, described in the next sections, have been widely accepted for synthesis of complex peptides. Their acceptance has been based, first, on the fact that they can be used with minimal loss of optical activity of the carboxyl component and, second, on a balance of convenience, freedom from side reactions, and practical yield.

MIXED ANHYDRIDES   Reaction of a carboxylic anhydride with an amine is a common method of N-acylation, but to use the symmetric anhydride of a peptide or N-protected amino acid would be wasteful of that component, since only half of it would actually provide an acyl group. However, certain mixed anhydrides, which react with amines only at the carbonyl of the N-protected aminoacyl component, can be used instead.

For peptide synthesis, mixed anhydrides of the carboxyl component with ethyl- or isobutylcarbonic acid are employed. These are prepared by a procedure standard for mixed anhydrides: reaction of a salt of one component with an acyl halide of the other. Usually, the triethylammonium salt of the peptide carboxyl component is used [Eq. (3–37)]. Synthesis of the anhydride is carried out in a non-

$$
\underset{\text{RC}}{\overset{\text{O}}{\overset{\|}{}}}\!\!-\!\text{O}^- + \underset{\text{Cl}}{\overset{\text{O}}{\overset{\|}{}}}\!\!-\!\text{C}\!-\!\text{OR}' \;\rightarrow\; \text{RC}\overset{\text{O}}{\overset{\|}{}}\!\!-\!\text{O}\!-\!\text{C}\overset{\text{O}}{\overset{\|}{}}\!\!-\!\text{OR}' + \text{Cl}^- \qquad (3\text{–}37)
$$

polar solvent, if possible, and at about $-10°C$. Formation of the anhydride is complete in a few minutes. The amino component is added directly to the reaction mixture, and the coupling is allowed to proceed at the low temperature [Eq. (3–38)]. Yields range between

$$RC\text{—}O\text{—}COR' + R''NH_2 \rightarrow RC\text{—}NHR'' + CO_2 + R'OH \quad (3\text{–}38)$$

40 and 95 per cent. A side reaction, avoided by use of low temperatures (below −5°C), is decomposition of the mixed anhydride to form an ester [Eq. (3–39)].

$$RC\text{—}O\text{—}COR' \rightarrow R\text{—}C\text{—}OR' + CO_2 \quad (3\text{–}39)$$

Mixed anhydrides other than carbonic also have been used for peptide coupling. These include those formed with derivatives of phosphoric and sulfuric acids as well as with sterically hindered carboxylic acids such as pivalic.

ACYL AZIDES   A peptide-coupling reaction that has withstood the test of long experience and was, in fact, one of the first to be developed (by Curtius in 1902), is reaction of the amino component with an acyl azide [Eq. (3–40)]. This is the only method of peptide

$$RC\text{—}N_3 + H_2NR' \rightarrow RC\text{—}NHR' + HN_3 \quad (3\text{–}40)$$

synthesis that does not lead to detectable racemization of the carboxyl component, regardless of its nature. Although it is a complicated procedure that often affords low yields, it is still one of the most widely used coupling techniques.

To form an acyl azide, a methyl or ethyl ester of the carboxyl component is first treated with hydrazine [Eq. (3–41)]. The acyl hydra-

$$RC\text{—}OMe + H_2NNH_2 \rightarrow RC\text{—}NHNH_2 + MeOH \quad (3\text{–}41)$$

zide so formed is usually crystalline and may be purified by recrystallization. It is then treated in aqueous acid with nitrous acid, or in an anhydrous acidic medium with an alkyl nitrite or nitrosyl chloride, to produce the acyl azide [Eq. (3-42)]. Isolation and purification of

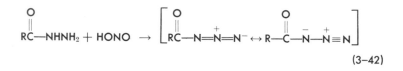

$$(3-42)$$

the azide is based on its solubility in organic solvents and insolubility in water.

All handling of an acyl azide must occur at low temperatures (below 5° C) to suppress the Curtius rearrangement. Although the Curtius rearrangement [Eq. (3-43)] to isocyanates and their deriva-

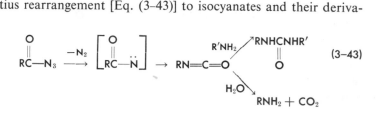

$$(3-43)$$

tives is a useful synthetic tool in other circumstances, its occurrence in peptide synthesis not only reduces peptide yields but makes product purification difficult.

The acyl azides couple with amino components in organic solvents, at 5° C or below. Over-all yields range between 30 and 70 per cent.

CARBODIIMIDES N,N'-dialkylcarbodiimides, available by dehydration or dethiolation of the corresponding ureas or thioureas [Eqs. (3-44) or (3-45)], are useful reagents for one-step peptide

$$
\begin{array}{c}
\text{O} \\
\| \\
\text{R—NH—C—NH—R} + C_6H_5SO_2Cl + Et_3N \rightarrow
\end{array}
$$

$$R—N{=}C{=}N—R + C_6H_5SO_3H + Et_3N^+HCl^- \qquad (3\text{-}44)$$

$$
\begin{array}{c}
\text{S} \\
\| \\
\text{R—NH—C—NH—R} + HgO \rightarrow R—N{=}C{=}NR + HgS + H_2O
\end{array}
$$

$$(3-45)$$

coupling. N,N'-dicyclohexyl carbodiimide was first exploited for use in formation of pyrophosphoric acid derivatives [Eq. (3-46)], but

$$2(RO)_2P(O)OH + C_6H_{11}N{=}C{=}NC_6H_{11} \rightarrow$$

$$\underset{}{(RO)_2P(O)OP(O)(OR)_2} + C_6H_{11}N{-}\overset{\overset{\displaystyle O}{\|}}{C}{-}NC_6H_{11} \qquad (3{-}46)$$

its utility in synthesis of carboxylic acid derivatives was soon established.

When a dialkylcarbodiimide is allowed to react with a carboxylic acid there is first formed an *O*-acyl urea [Eq. (3–47)]. The *O*-acyl

$$
\begin{array}{c}
R'N{=}C{=}NR' \\[4pt]
+ \\[4pt]
RCOOH
\end{array}
\rightarrow
\left[
\begin{array}{c}
R'N{=}C{-}NHR' \\[2pt]
| \\[2pt]
O \\[2pt]
| \\[2pt]
RCO
\end{array}
\right]
\qquad (3{-}47)
$$

urea reacts readily with nucleophiles. If an amine is present, an amide is formed [Eq. (3–48)]. If no other nucleophile is present, or

$$
\left[
\begin{array}{c}
\overset{\overset{\displaystyle O}{\|}}{RC}{-}O{-}\overset{\overset{\displaystyle NR'}{\|}}{C} \\[2pt]
| \\[2pt]
NHR'
\end{array}
\right]
+ R''NH_2 \rightarrow
\overset{\overset{\displaystyle O}{\|}}{RC}{-}NHR'' +
O{=}\overset{\overset{\displaystyle NHR'}{|}}{C}
\qquad (3{-}48)
$$

$$ NHR'$$

if reaction of those present is slow or hindered, the reactive intermediate undergoes rearrangement to a more stable *N*-acyl urea, which is only slightly susceptible to reaction with nucleophiles [Eq. (3–49)].

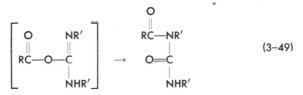

$$
\left[
\begin{array}{c}
\overset{\overset{\displaystyle O}{\|}}{RC}{-}O{-}\overset{\overset{\displaystyle NR'}{\|}}{C} \\[2pt]
| \\[2pt]
NHR'
\end{array}
\right]
\rightarrow
\begin{array}{c}
\overset{\overset{\displaystyle O}{\|}}{RC}{-}NR' \\[2pt]
| \\[2pt]
O{=}C \\[2pt]
| \\[2pt]
NHR'
\end{array}
\qquad (3{-}49)
$$

Dialkylcarbodiimide-induced acylation is not restricted to amines; phenols are converted to phenyl esters, and if excess carboxylic acid is the only available reactant, carboxylic anhydrides are formed.

N,N'-dicyclohexylcarbodiimide is the reagent most readily available for the reaction just described. The initial manipulations required for its use in peptide coupling are extremely simple: Amino and carboxyl components are mixed in as high concentration as possible; the solution is cooled to 0°, and the carbodiimide is added.

The presence of water does not seriously interfere with carbodiimide-induced peptide coupling, and therefore aqueous solvents can be used.

Occasionally, separation of dicyclohexylurea, the hydration product of the carbodiimide, from the peptide product is difficult. To meet this difficulty, dialkylcarbodiimides that yield water-soluble ureas have been devised. One example is N-(3-dimethylamino-propyl)-N'-ethylcarbodiimide hydrochloride:

$$[Me_2NH(CH_2)_3N{=}C{=}NEt]^+ \ Cl^-$$

ACTIVE ESTERS   Aminolysis of simple alkyl esters is usually slow. Phenyl esters are more reactive, because phenolate ions, being less basic than alkoxide ions (they are the conjugate bases of stronger acids) are better leaving groups. [See Eq. (3–36) and its discussion.] The acidity of a phenol, and thus the reactivity of its esters toward amines and other nucleophiles, is markedly increased by substitution of electron-withdrawing groups into the aromatic ring. Because of this, pentachlorophenyl esters have been introduced, and *p*-nitro-phenyl esters are currently in extensive use as activated carboxyl components in peptide synthesis. *p*-Nitrophenyl esters are prepared by reaction of the carboxyl component with *p*-nitrophenol, using N,N'-dicyclohexylcarbodiimide as the coupling agent [Eq.(3–50)].

$$RCOOH + HO\langle\ \rangle NO_2 + C_6H_{11}N{=}C{=}NC_6H_{11} \ \rightarrow$$

$$RCOO\langle\ \rangle NO_2 + C_6H_{11}NHCONHC_6H_{11} \qquad (3–50)$$

Benzyloxycarbonyl amino acid *p*-nitrophenyl esters are crystalline materials which, in contrast to other activated carboxyl derivatives, may be stored (in the dark) on the laboratory shelf. For coupling, the nitrophenyl ester and the amino component are mixed in a non-hydroxylic solvent and stored at room temperature [Eq. (3–51)].

$$\overset{O}{\overset{\|}{RC}}{-}O\langle\ \rangle NO_2 + R'NH_2 \rightarrow \overset{O}{\overset{\|}{RC}}NHR' + HO\langle\ \rangle NO_2 \quad (3–51)$$

Recovered yields of peptide product are usually high, often almost quantitative.

The nitrophenyl-ester method is especially useful in building a peptide chain by stepwise addition of single amino acid residues to the amino end of a growing chain. When this method is used, the step which might result in poor yields, formation of the active ester itself, occurs at the relatively inexpensive level of the benzyloxy-carbonyl amino acid.

3–5 Racemization

A satisfactory peptide synthesis must proceed without affecting configuration about any of the asymmetric centers of the components. In peptide work, formation of diasteromeric mixtures is at least as undesirable as formation of covalent bonds between the wrong atoms. In syntheses of physiologically active peptides, for example, it is important to know that any observed biological activity is a property of the molecule to which synthesis is directed, and not of traces of a highly active diastereomer. Unfortunately, it is often difficult to separate peptides that differ only in configuration. Avoiding racemization of optically active centers is therefore a major concern in planning peptide syntheses.

Normally, the only asymmetric center in danger of losing its optical integrity during peptide bond formation is the α-carbon adjacent to the activated carboxyl group. Racemization of this center occurs largely through formation of an intermediate 5-oxazolone (azlactone), which can be formed, often reversibly, from any acyl derivative of an N-acyl-α-amino acid that is sufficiently electrophilic to undergo the internal nucleophilic attack illustrated in Eq. (3–52).

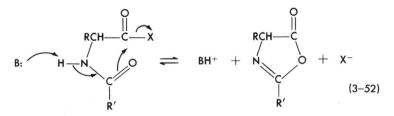

$$(3\text{--}52)$$

5-Oxazolones form resonance-stabilized anions in which the initially asymmetric center takes on a trigonal-bond arrangement. Any weak base present in a solution containing the oxazolone, even the solvent itself, can catalyze loss of optical activity *via* the oxazolone anion, even though anion formation is not favored at equilibrium [Eq. (3–53)].

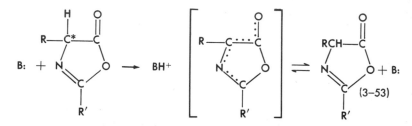

(3–53)

Equilibrium formation of the oxazolone itself need not be extensive to effect racemization, but the cyclization of Eq. (3–52) does not in any event interfere with peptide coupling, because 5-oxazolones themselves react with amines to form amides [Eq. (3–54)].

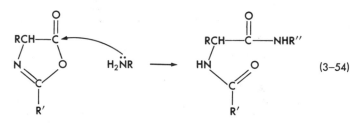

(3–54)

Evidence supporting the oxazolone mechanism for racemization includes spectrophotometric identification of oxazolones in solutions of acylamino *p*-nitrophenyl esters, as well as kinetic studies of the rates of racemization and ring opening of optically active oxazolones.

Racemization of optically active carboxyl derivatives has also been observed to occur in circumstances where azlactone formation is impossible or unlikely. In these cases, the path involved is probably direct ionization of the proton from the α-carbon of the amino acid derivative. This C—H group is less acidic than the corresponding group in a 5-oxazolone, but its anion is still resonance-stabilized and similarly incapable of retaining asymmetry:

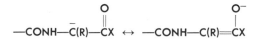

By proper attention to the factors affecting racemization, peptide coupling processes and peptide syntheses can be designed so that the loss of optical activity is minimized. The observed facts are these:

1. Regardless of the activation and coupling method, racemization is minimized by use of the least polar solvent possible.

2. Racemization is favored by the presence of any base over and above the necessary amino group of the second component.

3. Racemization is favored by higher temperature.

4. Proline derivatives are not readily racemized. [An N-acyl proline derivative, which lacks an N—H group, cannot cyclize by the mechanism of Eq. (3–52).]

5. N-phthaloyl and N-toluenesulfonyl derivatives do not readily racemize. (These, of course, cannot form 5-oxazolones.)

6. N-Alkoxycarbonyl amino acid derivatives do not racemize on activation. (Conceivably these do not readily form 5-oxazolones. However, a process akin to that cyclization leads to formation of N-carboxy anhydrides from benzyloxycarbonylaminoacyl halides. See Section 3–8.)

7. N-acyl-α-aminoacyl azides do not racemize. The reason for this is not clear.

3–6   Peptide Notation

Structural formulas of peptides are unwieldy when written in full, and an internationally agreed upon shorthand notation for them has been adopted. In this notation the abbreviations given in Table 2–1 are used to indicate the amino acids themselves. The amino group is considered to be at the left side of the three-letter symbol, and substitution for one of its protons is indicated by a dash. The carboxyl is at the right, and replacement of its hydroxyl part is similarly indicated. Substitution on a side-chain functional group is indicated by a vertical line. Use of the system is illustrated in Figure 3–2.

Peptides are written with the amino end of the chain at the left. If ambiguity is possible, peptide bonds are indicated by an arrow joining the abbreviations for the amino acids. The arrow points from the carbonyl to the amino group.

Unless otherwise indicated, the abbreviations stand for amino acids of the L series.

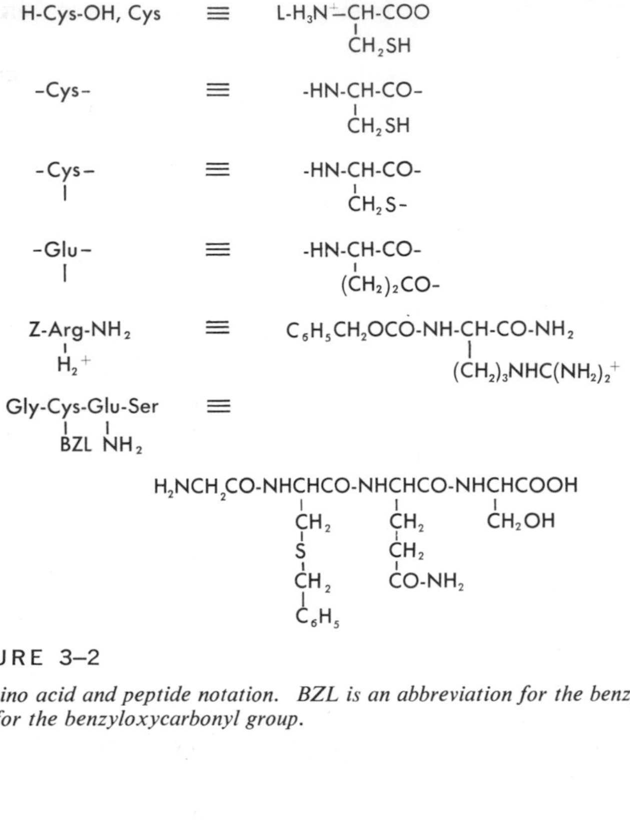

$$\text{H-Cys-OH, Cys} \equiv \underset{\underset{\displaystyle CH_2SH}{|}}{L\text{-}H_3N\text{--}CH\text{-}COO}$$

$$-\text{Cys}- \equiv \underset{\underset{\displaystyle CH_2SH}{|}}{-HN\text{-}CH\text{-}CO-}$$

$$\underset{\displaystyle |}{-\text{Cys}-} \equiv \underset{\underset{\displaystyle CH_2S-}{|}}{-HN\text{-}CH\text{-}CO-}$$

$$\underset{\displaystyle |}{-\text{Glu}-} \equiv \underset{\underset{\displaystyle (CH_2)_2CO-}{|}}{-HN\text{-}CH\text{-}CO-}$$

$$\underset{\underset{\displaystyle H_2{}^+}{|}}{\text{Z-Arg-NH}_2} \equiv \underset{\underset{\displaystyle (CH_2)_3NHC(NH_2)_2{}^+}{|}}{C_6H_5CH_2OCO\text{-}NH\text{-}CH\text{-}CO\text{-}NH_2}$$

$$\underset{\underset{\displaystyle BZL \quad NH_2}{|\quad\;|}}{\text{Gly-Cys-Glu-Ser}} \equiv$$

H₂NCH₂CO-NHCHCO-NHCHCO-NHCHCOOH

with side chains:
- CH₂—S—CH₂—C₆H₅
- CH₂—CH₂—CO-NH₂
- CH₂OH

FIGURE 3–2

*Amino acid and peptide notation. BZL is an abbreviation for the benzyl group;
Z, for the benzyloxycarbonyl group.*

3–7 Synthesis of Complex Peptides

With properly blocked and activated amino acid derivatives it
is possible to build up a peptide chain in three ways: (1) by addition
of one amino acid residue at a time to the carboxyl end of a growing
chain, (2) by addition of one residue at a time to the amino end of
a growing chain, and (3) by condensation of separately constructed
fragments, each containing only a few amino acid residues. Stepwise synthesis by repeated couplings at the carboxyl end of a growing peptide chain is impractical, because racemization is apt to
occur when the carboxyl group is activated. However, since activated *N*-alkoxycarbonyl amino acids do not racemize, stepwise
synthesis using these derivatives as carboxyl components is a
highly satisfactory procedure.

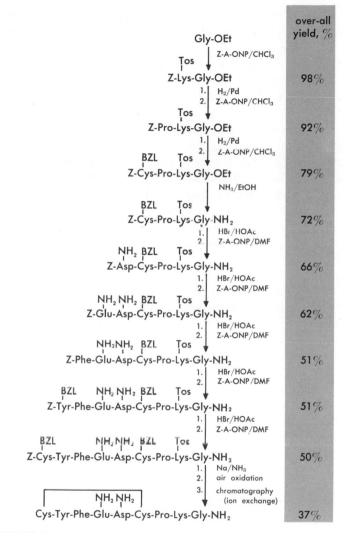

over-all yield, %

Gly-OEt

Z-A-ONP/CHCl₃

Tos

Z-Lys-Gly-OEt   98%

1. H₂/Pd
2. Z-A-ONP/CHCl₃

Tos

Z-Pro-Lys-Gly-OEt   92%

1. H₂/Pd
2. Z-A-ONP/CHCl₃

BZL   Tos

Z-Cys-Pro-Lys-Gly-OEt   79%

NH₃/EtOH

BZL   Tos

Z-Cys-Pro-Lys-Gly-NH₂   72%

1. HBr/HOAc
2. Z-A-ONP/DMF

NH₂ BZL   Tos

Z-Asp-Cys-Pro-Lys-Gly-NH₂   66%

1. HBr/HOAc
2. Z-A-ONP/DMF

NH₂ NH₂ BZL   Tos

Z-Glu-Asp-Cys-Pro-Lys-Gly-NH₂   62%

1. HBr/HOAc
2. Z-A-ONP/DMF

NH₂ NH₂ BZL   Tos

Z-Phe-Glu-Asp-Cys-Pro-Lys-Gly-NH₂   51%

1. HBr/HOAc
2. Z-A-ONP/DMF

BZL   NH₂ NH₂ BZL   Tos

Z-Tyr-Phe-Glu-Asp-Cys-Pro-Lys-Gly-NH₂   51%

1. HBr/HOAc
2. Z-A-ONP/DMF

BZL   NH₂ NH₂ BZL   Tos

Z-Cys-Tyr-Phe-Glu-Asp-Cys-Pro-Lys-Gly-NH₂   50%

1. Na/NH₃
2. air oxidation
3. chromatography (ion exchange)

NH₂ NH₂

Cys-Tyr-Phe-Glu-Asp-Cys-Pro-Lys-Gly-NH₂   37%

FIGURE 3–3

Synthesis of lysine vasopressin by addition of single residues. All intermediates shown are crystalline and the product has full biological potency. Abbreviations: Tos, p-toluenesulfonyl; Z, benzyloxycarbonyl; BZL, benzyl; Z-A-ONP, N-benzyloxycarbonylamino acid p-nitrophenyl ester; DMF, dimethylformamide.

An example of synthesis by stepwise addition of single residues is the preparation, shown in Figure 3-3, of the nonapeptide, lysine vasopressin (see Section 6-1). As is seen in the figure, an *N*-protected amino acid, activated as its *p*-nitrophenyl ester, is coupled with a carboxyl-protected amino component. The fully protected peptide product of this coupling is treated to remove only the *N*-terminal protecting group, and the resultant is then used as the amino component in the next step. The high over-all yield points to a major advantage of coupling *via* nitrophenyl esters.

During the synthesis shown in Figure 3-3, the growing peptide chain was purified by crystallization after the addition of each new residue. The final product, once salts introduced by the sodium in liquid ammonia cleavage had been removed, was therefore quite pure, even before a final ion exchange chromatographic step. Had there been no intermediate purification steps, obtaining a satisfactory product would have been much more difficult.

In a recently developed peptide synthesis, utilizing single residue addition, potential difficulty in final purification is accepted in return for convenience and speed in building up the chain. In this procedure, the growing peptide chain is attached to an insoluble polymer. The method is illustrated in Figure 3-4. A lightly cross-linked, and therefore highly porous, polystyrene resin is chloromethylated. The chloromethyl polymer which is, in effect, a benzyl halide, is treated with the salt of a *t*-butoxycarbonyl amino acid in ethanol. An insoluble polymer ester is formed, from which salts and unbound by-products may readily be washed, but to which, because of the porous form of the resin, access by other reagents is easy. The *t*-butoxycarbonyl *N*-protecting group of the resin ester is removed by treatment with hydrochloric acid in acetic acid. The resulting aminoacyl resin is thoroughly washed and then treated with excess of another *t*-butoxycarbonyl amino acid plus dicyclohexylcarbodiimide. Coupling occurs, and one then has a blocked dipeptidyl resin, which can be washed free of dicyclohexylurea, again treated with acid to free the terminal amino group, and so on. At each step the growing peptide, bound to the resin, is isolated merely by filtering. When the chain has been completely constructed, the peptide is liberated from the resin by treatment with hydrogen bromide in trifluoroacetic acid.

Satisfactory use of the resin technique requires that all coupling and *N*-unblocking steps proceed in high yield, because peptide im-

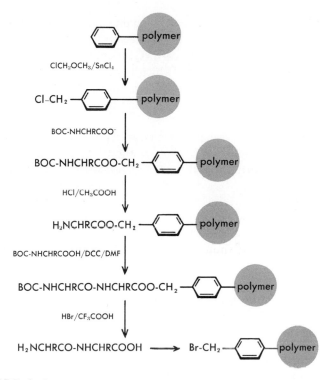

FIGURE 3–4

Dipeptide synthesis using a polystyrene resin support. Abbreviations: BOC, t-butoxycarbonyl; DCC, dicyclohexylcarbodiimide; DMF, dimethylformamide.

purities are carried along until the peptide is finally removed from the resin. In spite of this disadvantage, the method has been successfully applied to the synthesis of a physiologically active nonapeptide, bradykinin (see Section 6–1), in an over-all yield of 68 per cent.

Syntheses via stepwise addition of single residues is not always practical. Purification and handling of peptides become more difficult as chains get longer and as more functional groups are present. Solubility in organic solvents decreases with increasing peptide size. The inevitable losses at each step also become more expensive as the molecule grows. Further, the necessary flexibility in choice of protecting groups may not be attainable.

In a properly designed synthesis using previously prepared peptide fragments, it is still possible to avoid racemization. This is done by choosing fragments to end in carboxyl-terminal glycine (which is not optically active) or proline (which is racemized only with difficulty). If this cannot be done, racemization may be avoided by using the azide coupling procedure to join the fragments, at perhaps some cost in yield.

An example of the synthesis of a large peptide from smaller fragments is given in Figure 3–5. The synthesis shown is of a physiologically active portion of the adrenocorticotropic hormone (see Section 6–1). *t*-Butyl-based protecting groups were used for protection of terminal and side-chain amino and carboxy groups. Thus relatively mild conditions, treatment with trifluoroacetic acid, could be used to generate the physiologically active peptide from its blocked precursor. It should be noted that the fragments 5–10, 11–14, and 15–19 end in glycine or proline. Coupling of peptide 1–10 with peptide 11–24 by use of dicyclohexylcarbodiimide would have occurred with racemization if there had been an optically active residue at position 10. The fragment 1–4, which ends in methionine, is activated as the azide, so that racemization does not occur in coupling it with peptide 5–10. ·

In any synthesis of a complex peptide it is usually necessary to monitor the optical purity of the intermediates and product. Crystallinity may be an indication that a substance is optically pure, but it is not necessarily so, and many peptides, no matter how pure, cannot be obtained in the crystalline form. Optical rotation is usually of little value, because the rotations of the desired product and all the possible impurities are rarely known. A satisfactory method of determining optical purity, if L-amino acids are used, is to subject the product to enzymatic hydrolysis (Section 5–4). Racemization is indicated by incomplete hydrolysis by an enzyme known to catalyze hydrolysis only of L-amino acid derivatives.

3–8 Amino Acid Polymers

Peptide chains containing over 30 amino acid units, varying in kind and linked in a known sequence, have been prepared by stepwise peptide synthesis. The cost of these peptides in man-hours is high, and the amounts that can be produced are small. Homoge-

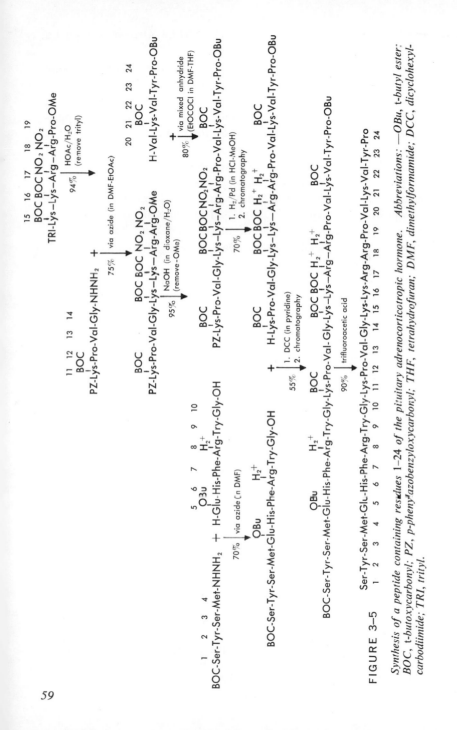

FIGURE 3-5 Synthesis of a peptide containing residues 1–24 of the pituitary adrenocorticotropic hormone. Abbreviations: —OBu, t-butyl ester; BOC, t-butoxycarbonyl; PZ, p-phenylazobenzyloxycarbonyl; THF, tetrahydrofuran; DMF, dimethylformamide; DCC, dicyclohexyl-carbodiimide; TRI, trityl.

neous peptides of higher molecular weight and defined sequence have so far been produced only by nature.

In the laboratory, however, mixtures of peptides containing hundreds or thousands of amino acid units can be prepared by polymerization. These mixtures may be called amino acid polymers, to distinguish them from the better-defined substances produced by nature or by stepwise laboratory syntheses. Like the products of all polymerizations, amino acid polymers are not homogeneous, that is, the molecules in a sample are not all identical in length, composition, or sequence. Nonetheless, they are of considerable interest, especially the homopolymeric ones (one kind of amino acid residue), as models for the physicochemical behavior of proteins.

N-CARBOXY ANHYDRIDES   At present, the only satisfactory method for preparing clean polymers of α-amino acids is based on the ring-opening polymerization of amino acid *N*-carboxy anhydrides, which are also known, after their discoverer, as Leuchs' anhydrides. These cyclic mixed anhydrides of carbonic acid and an amino acid are most simply prepared by reaction of phosgene with a dioxane suspension of the amino acid [Eq. (2–16)]. As the anhydride is formed, the amino acid dissolves.

An alternative method of synthesis begins with the *N*-benzyloxycarbonyl derivative of the amino acid. Treatment with an inorganic acid halide, such as thionyl chloride, phosphorus pentachloride, or phosphorus tribromide, if carried out at low temperature, results in formation of the corresponding acyl halide [Eq. (3–55)]. When

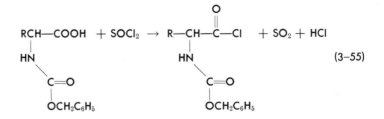

the reaction is carried out at room temperature or above, however, cyclization occurs with cleavage of the benzyl-oxygen bond, and the *N*-carboxy anhydride is formed [Eq. (3–56)].

For the preparation of *N*-carboxy anhydrides by either method, side-chain functional groups are protected. Benzyl esters are used

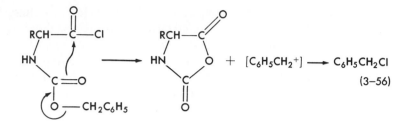

$$(3\text{-}56)$$

for aspartic and glutamic acids, and ϵ-N-benzyloxycarbonyl groups for lysine.

Polymerization of N-carboxy anhydrides may be initiated by nucleophiles, frequently primary amines. These react by addition to the 5-carbonyl of the ring (the one corresponding to the carboxyl of the original amino acid). The ring is opened and an intermediate carbamic acid derivative is formed. The carbamic acid decarboxylates to generate a new amino group, which in turn reacts with another molecule of anhydride, and so on. The process is illustrated in Eqs. (3–57) through (3–59). Average degrees of polymerization up to several hundred have been achieved in this way.

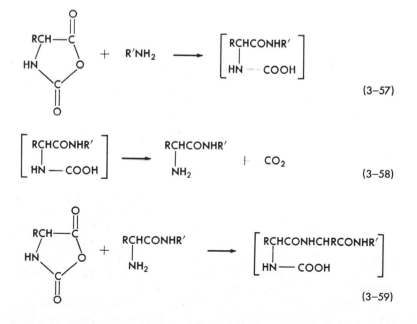

$$(3\text{-}57)$$

$$(3\text{-}58)$$

$$(3\text{-}59)$$

When aprotic bases, for example, sodium methoxide or tertiary amines, are used as initiators, polymerization proceeds by a different mechanism, one which usually has a higher rate and often leads to higher degrees of polymerization. In this path, the first step is not addition to the 5-carbonyl group, but abstraction of a proton from the N—H group [Eq. (3–60)]. Addition of the anhydride anion to another molecule of anhydride is the next step [Eq. (3–61)], but

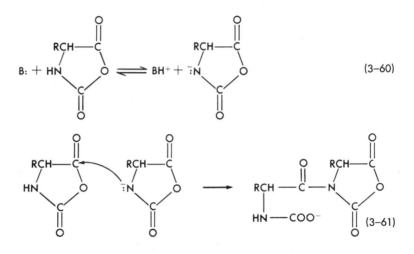

(3–60)

(3–61)

subsequent steps have not been established with certainty. It is known that they do not involve reaction of anhydride with a free amino group [as in Eq. (3–59)]. With this kind of initiation, amino acid polymers thousands of units in length have been obtained.

All the naturally occurring amino acids, most of their enantiomorphs, and many other α-amino acids have been polymerized via their *N*-carboxy anhydrides. Yields are high, and the reactions proceed at room temperature. Racemization, if it occurs, has not been reported. Copolymers of amino acids can be made from mixtures of the anhydrides. These are generally called random, although they are not precisely so; those residues which polymerize faster are concentrated at one end of the chain. Polymers and copolymers prepared from *N*-carboxy anhydrides have found no commercial application, even though they could perhaps be prepared with the properties of silk or wool; their cost is too high.

TRIPEPTIDE POLYMERS   Methods for polymerizing small peptides, to give polymers with regularly repeating sequences of amino acid residues, have been much sought after. Polymerization of dipeptide derivatives is an unfavorable process, since diketopiperazines (Section 2–3) are usually the major products. However, carboxyl-activated tripeptides, bearing an unprotected terminal α-amino group, can be condensed to give polymers; polymers containing up to 20 to 25 tripeptide units have been formed in very concentrated solutions of tripeptide-active esters. The *p*-nitrophenyl and pentachlorophenyl esters seem useful for this purpose. An example is given in Figure 3–6. Yields of poly(tripeptides) are not always high, however. Cyclodimerization to form cyclic hexapeptides is a known competing reaction [Eq. (3–62)].

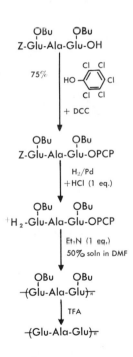

FIGURE 3–6

Preparation of a repeating sequence polymer from a tripeptide. Polymer of molecular weight about 20,000 was obtained in about 20 per cent yield from the benzyloxycarbonyltripeptide pentachlorophenyl ester. Abbreviations: Z, benzyloxycarbonyl; DCC, dicyclohexylcarbodiimide; DMF, dimethylformamide; TFA, trifluoroacetic acid; PCP, pentachlorophenyl.

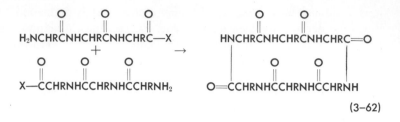

$$(3\text{-}62)$$

Condensation polymerization of α-amino acid derivatives has not been a successful general method for preparation of amino acid polymers. ϵ-Aminocaproic acid, or longer chain ω-amino acids, are converted to high yields of polyamides on heating at about 200°C [Eq. (3-63)], but pyrolysis of dry, neutral α-amino acids usually

$$H_2N(CH_2)_{10}COOH \xrightarrow{\ 220°\ } \{NH(CH_2)_{10}CO\}_n + nH_2O \qquad (3\text{-}63)$$

results in deamination and decarboxylation. Heating α-amino acids in glycerol (180 to 200°C), a technique used for preparation of diketopiperazines, does in some cases afford polymers as well; glyceryl esters are probably intermediates.

References

Reviews

N. F. Albertson, "Synthesis of Peptides with Mixed Anhydrides," *Org. Reactions,* **12,** 157–355 (1962).

R. A. Boissonnas, "Selectively Removable Amino Protective Groups Used in the Synthesis of Peptides," *Advan. Org. Chem.,* **3,** 159–190 (1963).

M. Goodman and G. W. Kenner, "The Synthesis of Peptides," *Advan. Protein Chem.,* **12,** 465–626 (1957).

J. P. Greenstein and M. Winitz, "Chemical Procedures for the Synthesis of Peptides," in *Chemistry of the Amino Acids,* Vol. 2, Wiley, New York, 1961, Chap. 10, pp. 763–1295.

K. Hofmann and P. G. Katsoyannis, "Synthesis and Function of Peptides of Biological Interest," in H. Neurath (ed.), *The Proteins,* Vol. I, 2nd ed., Academic Press, New York, 1963, pp. 53–188.

E. Katchalski and M. Sela, "Synthesis and Chemical Properties of Poly-α-Amino Acids," *Advan. Protein Chem.,* **13,** 244–492 (1958).

J. F. W. McOmie, "Protective Groups," *Advan. Org. Chem.*, **3**, 191–294 (1963).

J. Meienhofer, "Synthesen biologisch wirksamer Peptide," *Chimia*, **16**, 385–424 (1962).

E. Schröder and K. Lübke, *The Peptides*, Vols. 1 and 2, translated by E. Gross, Academic Press, New York, 1965.

T. Wieland and H. Determann, "Methods of Peptide Synthesis," *Angew. Chem. Int. Ed.*, **2**, 358–370 (1963).

Papers

M. Goodman and L. Levine, "Peptide Synthesis via Active Esters; Racemization and Ring Opening of Optically Active Oxazolones," *J. Am. Chem. Soc.*, **86**, 2918–2922 (1964).

J. Kovacs and A. Kapoor, "Synthesis of Polypeptides with Known Repeating Sequences of Amino Acids," *J. Am. Chem. Soc.*, **87**, 118–119 (1965).

R. B. Merrifield, "Solid-Phase Peptide Synthesis. An Improved Synthesis of Bradykinin," *Biochemistry*, **3**, 1385–1390 (1964).

R. B. Merrifield, "Automated Synthesis of Peptides," *Science*, **150**, 178–185 (1965).

R. Schwyzer, et al., "Report of the Committee on Nomenclature," in G. T. Young (ed.), *Peptides*, Macmillan, New York, 1963, pp. 261–269.

4

▪ DETERMINING THE COVALENT
STRUCTURE OF PEPTIDES

4–1 Amino Acid Analysis

DETERMINATION OF AMINO ACID COMPOSITION is a necessary first step comparable to the determination of a molecular formula, toward establishing the *primary*, or covalent, structure of a peptide.

Peptides or proteins are usually hydrolyzed to mixtures of their constituent amino acids by 24-hour treatment with 6 N hydrochloric acid at 105°C. The amino acids are recovered by evaporation of the hydrochloric acid. Tryptophan, because of its acid-sensitive indole nucleus, and, to a lesser extent, some of the other amino acids are partially destroyed under these conditions, but in quantitative studies corrections may be made for the losses. Glutamine and asparagine residues are converted to ammonia plus glutamic and aspartic acids. Sterically hindered peptide bonds, involving the carboxyl group of valine or isoleucine, may require longer treatment for complete hydrolysis.

Identification of the amino acids in a peptide hydrolyzate may be carried out by two-dimensional paper chromatography (Section A–1), but the quantitative accuracy of this technique is not high. At present, the most satisfactory method for quantitative separation and analysis of amino acid mixtures utilizes chromatography on columns of ion exchange resins (Section A–2). Automated equipment for this analysis is commercially available. In this apparatus, a hydrolyzate is passed through columns of a sulfonic acid ion exchange resin, using sodium citrate buffer solutions as elutants. Carefully controlled and reproducible conditions are used, so that each amino acid is identified by the volume of buffer required to elute it from the column. Two columns are used, one operated at pH 5.3, to separate the basic amino acids, ammonia, and tryptophan, and the other, operated at pH 3.25 and 4.25, to separate other amino acids. Effluent from these columns is mixed with a ninhydrin reagent (Section 2–3) and heated under controlled conditions. It then passes through a spectrophotometer for measurement of the optical absorption of the ninhydrin reaction products. The results are recorded continuously. Figure 4–1 indicates the sort of recorder trace obtained. Amino acid composition of the original hydrolyzate is determined from this recorder output; the position of an absorption peak identifies the residue, and the area under the peak, with corrections for color yields, gives the quantity. The process requires about 24 hours and can be carried out with 3 per cent accuracy for as little as 0.1 micromole of an amino acid.

The number of amino acid analyses that must be carried out in establishing the structure of even a relatively small protein is so large that more rapid and more sensitive methods are desirable. Both mass spectrometry and gas-phase chromatography have been shown to be capable of analyzing mixtures of extremely small amounts of amino acid mixtures. Amino acids themselves are not sufficiently volatile for analysis by gas-phase chromatography, although some of their derivatives are suitable. Esters and N-trifluoroacetyl esters have been used for gas-chromatographic analysis, but quantitative conversion to these derivatives is difficult. Trimethylsilyl derivatives, conveniently prepared by treatment of the amino acid mixture with N,O-bis(trimethylsilyl) acetamide [Eq. (4–1)], appear promising.

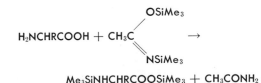

$$\text{H}_2\text{NCHRCOOH} + \text{CH}_3\text{C} \overset{\text{OSiMe}_3}{\underset{\text{NSiMe}_3}{\Big\langle}} \rightarrow$$

$$\text{Me}_3\text{SiNHCHRCOOSiMe}_3 + \text{CH}_3\text{CONH}_2 \qquad (4\text{–}1)$$

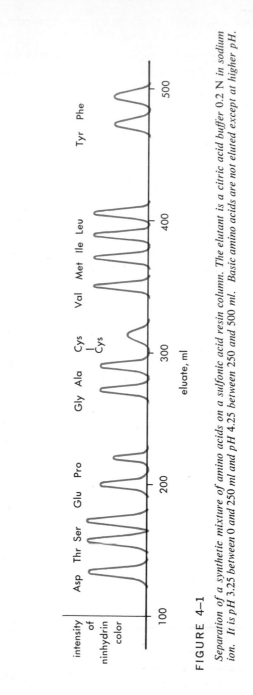

FIGURE 4-1

Separation of a synthetic mixture of amino acids on a sulfonic acid resin column. The elutant is a citric acid buffer 0.2 N in sodium ion. It is pH 3.25 between 0 and 250 ml and pH 4.25 between 250 and 500 ml. Basic amino acids are not eluted except at higher pH.

4–2 End-Group Analysis

Only a part of the structural information contained in a peptide is given by its amino acid composition. There are factorial N possible linear arrangements of N different amino acid residues; a pentapeptide composed of five different L-series residues may be one of 120 isomers. Therefore it is necessary to establish not only amino acid composition, but also amino acid sequence.

In each of the six structural isomers of a tripeptide of amino acid composition (A, B, C), one amino acid residue has a free α-amino group (called the *N-terminal* residue), one has a free carboxyl group (the *C-terminal* residue), and the third, in the middle, is bound by both its functional groups. The sequence of a tripeptide of known composition is established by applying chemical tests to distinguish the terminal amino acid residues.

Several end-group analyses have proved valuable in peptide work. One of these, dinitrophenylation, was developed by Frederick Sanger, about 1945, and used extensively by him in the first complete sequence determination of a protein, insulin.

DINITROPHENYLATION   Dinitrophenylation is a method for determining the N-terminal residue of a peptide chain, and utilizes the fact that 1-fluoro-2,4-dinitrobenzene (FDNB) reacts smoothly with a terminal α-amino group, in bicarbonate-buffered aqueous ethanol, to form an N-(2,4-dinitrophenyl) derivative [Eq. (4–2)]

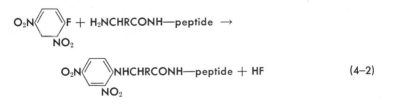

$$\tag{4-2}$$

The reaction is a bimolecular nucleophilic substitution process, facilitated by the electron-withdrawing nitro groups *ortho* and *para* to the site of nucleophilic attack, and is not specific for terminal α-amino groups. FDNB also reacts with other nucleophiles present in the peptide, for example, ϵ-amino of lysine, sulfhydryl of cysteine, and imidazole of histidine, but only the N-terminal residue reacts at its α-nitrogen.

When the dinitrophenylated peptide is hydrolyzed by acid, the

N_α-dinitrophenyl amino acid is readily separated from the other hydrolysis products. Because the strong electron-withdrawing effect of the dinitrophenyl group reduces the basicity of its α-amino nitrogen, the N_α-derivative may be extracted from the acidic hydrolysis mixture. It is then identified by paper chromatography, a process aided by its yellow color (λ_{max} 360 millimicrons); once so purified, it may be eluted from the paper and estimated spectrophotometrically if desired.

The Sanger technique permits only identification of the N-terminal residue of a peptide, because complete hydrolysis is necessary to obtain that residue for identification. However, less than a micromole of peptide is necessary for the whole procedure. By use of C^{14}-labeled FDNB and autoradiography of the paper chromatogram, this quantity can be reduced to 0.001 micromole. Since the N_α-dinitrophenyl amino acid can be determined quantitatively, the dinitrophenylation procedure may be used to establish the molecular weight of a peptide or protein, if the number of its N-terminal residues can otherwise be established. (Not all proteins are single, unbranched chains.)

EDMAN DEGRADATION   An end-group analysis known as the Edman degradation permits stepwise removal and identification of amino acids from the N-terminus *without* complete destruction of the peptide chain. In this process, the peptide is allowed to react with phenylisothiocyanate, to form an N-phenylthiocarbamyl peptide. Upon treatment with acid, this derivative cyclizes first to a thiazolone, and the terminal peptide bond is thereby broken. The cyclization is generally carried out in anhydrous media (hydrogen chloride in nitromethane or acetic acid), and in this same step the thiazolone rearranges to the more stable thiohydantoin. The overall process is shown in Eqs. (4–3), (4–4), and (4–5). The thiohydantoin,

$$C_6H_5N{=}C{=}S + H_2NCHRCONH\text{—peptide} \xrightarrow{\text{pH 8–9}}$$

$$\underset{\underset{S}{\overset{\|}{}}}{C_6H_5NHCNHCHRCONH}\text{—peptide} \qquad (4\text{–}3)$$

which is soluble in organic solvents, is separated from the abbreviated peptide chain and identified by paper chromatography. The residual peptide itself may be treated again with phenylisothio-

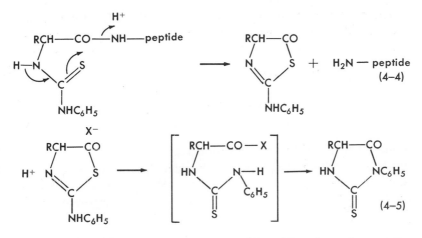

cyanate. In this manner as many as 10 residues have been successively removed and identified from 1 micromole of peptide. In a useful modification, the protein or peptide remains absorbed on a strip of filter paper for ease of handling throughout the process. In some instances it has proved convenient to identify the N-terminal residue by difference. For this purpose, a small portion of the residual peptide is removed and analyzed after each Edman cycle.

The number of Edman cycles that can usefully be applied to a given sample of peptide is limited. Because each cycle does not result in precisely quantitative removal of the N-terminal residue, and since the abbreviated peptide is not purified after each step, confusing mixtures of phenylthiohydantoins may result from later cycles.

HYDRAZINOLYSIS   Chemical methods for removing and identifying the C-terminal residue have not been quite so successful as the two N-terminal analyses just described. Strenuous treatment of a peptide or protein with anhydrous hydrazine (12 hours, 100°C) results in solvolysis of peptide bonds and formation of aminoacyl hydrazides. The carboxyl group of the C-terminal amino acid is not attacked. (In hydrazine, solvent carboxyl groups exist as carboxylate ion, which is highly resistant to nucleophilic addition.) Hydrazinolysis of a peptide thus liberates the C-terminal residue as a free amino acid [Eq. (4–6)].

$$H_2NCHRCO(NHCHRCO)_nNHCHR'COOH + (n + 1)NH_2NH_2 \rightarrow$$

$$(n + 1)H_2NCHRCONHNH_2 + H_2NCHR'COOH \qquad (4–6)$$

After removal of excess hydrazine, the hydrazinolyzed product is treated with FDNB, which converts the hydrazides to bis(dinitrophenyl) derivatives [Eq. (4–7)] and the free amino acid to an N_α-

$$2FDNB + H_2NCHRCONHNH_2 \rightarrow$$

$$O_2N\langle\rangle-NHCHRCONHNH-\langle\rangle NO_2 + 2HF \qquad (4\text{–}7)$$
$$\quad NO_2 \qquad\qquad\qquad\qquad NO_2$$

dinitrophenyl derivative. The former are soluble in organic solvents but insoluble in aqueous bicarbonate. Separated on this basis, the latter is identified by paper chromatography. About 1 micromole of peptide is required, and it is completely destroyed in the determination.

4–3 Determining Peptide Sequences

By use of total amino acid analysis, end-group determinations, and an additional tool, partial hydrolysis, one can establish the amino acid sequence of large peptides. The method may be illustrated as follows. Consider the pentapeptide

A—B—C—D—E

By use of the Sanger procedure and hydrazinolysis, residues A and E can be located at the N- and C-terminal positions, respectively. Partial acid hydrolysis of the original peptide (perhaps 12 N hydrochloric acid, 48 hours, 25°C) might yield, among other fragments, three smaller peptides of composition

(A,B,C)   (B,C,D,E)   (D,E)

that can be separated and purified in quantities sufficient for further examination. Because the position of residue E is already known, the position of D in the original chain is established by the isolation of (D,E), and the structure of the pentapeptide may thus be written

A—(B,C)—D—E

If the tetrapeptide is subjected to dinitrophenylation and hydrolysis, residue B is established as its N-terminus, and since it already contains D and E, known to be the next-to-last and last residues of the pentapeptide, its sequence is established as

B—C—D—E

and the over-all sequence must be

$$A—B—C—D—E$$

An alternative process might have involved partial acid hydrolysis of the dinitrophenyl pentapeptide. If the fragments DNP—(A,B,C, D), DNP—(A,B,C), DNP—(A,B) and DNP—A can be separated from the hydrolyzate and their composition determined, the sequence of the pentapeptide immediately follows.

The case chosen above is a simple one, in that the original peptide is small and no residue appears twice, but the principles are the same when large protein molecules are under study: reconstruction of the complete sequence from data gathered on a sufficient number of smaller overlapping fragments. For large molecules the process is tedious, involving many composition analyses and end-group determinations, and considerable bookkeeping on their results, plus the difficult task of isolating and purifying the necessary numerous fragments of the original molecule.

Acid hydrolysis of peptide bonds is a relatively nonspecific process, although not all peptide bonds are hydrolyzed at the same rate. Partial acid hydrolysis of a large peptide usually gives rise to too many fragments, and too little of each, for use in sequence studies. More specific methods of peptide cleavage, which afford only a limited number of fragments, and these in higher yield, are usually necessary.

4–4 Specific Cleavage of Peptides

ENZYMATIC HYDROLYSIS The most useful reagents for specific cleavage of peptide bonds have been provided by nature; these are the *proteolytic enzymes* (see Section 6–2).

To incorporate foreign protein into its own structure, an organism first breaks it down to the constituent amino acids, which it subsequently uses to synthesize protein to its own specifications. The breakdown process, digestion, is facilitated by catalysts, themselves proteins, which effect the hydrolysis of peptide bonds under conditions prevailing in the organism. These conditions are much milder than those required for acid hydrolysis, and an enzyme is much more specific with regard to the structures susceptible to its action than are nonenzymatic chemical reagents.

Many proteolytic enzymes have been identified, but only a few are available in sufficient purity and quantity, are sufficiently stable, and have appropriate specificities for use in peptide structure work. Those of major importance are listed below; all are specific for derivatives of L-amino acids. They may be divided into two classes, *endopeptidases*, which cleave internal peptide bonds, and *exopeptidases*, which bring about hydrolysis of terminal residues.

Trypsin is obtained from pancreas and attacks specifically at peptide bonds involving the carboxyl of lysine or arginine.

Chymotrypsin is also elaborated by pancreas. It preferentially attacks bonds involving the carboxyl of the aromatic amino acids tyrosine, tryptophan, and phenylalanine, but also catalyses hydrolysis of leucyl, methionyl, asparaginyl, and glutamyl peptide bonds.

Pepsin, obtained from gastric juice, *subtilisin*, produced by *Bacillus subtilis*, and *papain*, isolated from papaya latex, are endopeptidases of low specificity. Papain and subtilisin are particularly useful when it is desired to reduce a larger peptide to a small group of di- and tri-peptides.

Leucine aminopeptidase is an exopeptidase obtained from kidney. It hydrolyzes *N*-terminal peptide bonds to all common L-series amino acids but proline.

Carboxypeptidases are exopeptidases obtained from pancreas; they attack *C*-terminal peptide bonds.

The procedure for use of proteolytic enzymes usually involves incubation of a buffered solution of the peptide or protein to be digested with 1 to 2 per cent by weight of the enzyme. (Most enzymes listed function near neutrality; pepsin operates best near pH 2.) Reaction time is a matter of hours at room temperature or 37°C. Volatile buffers, such as ammonium carbonate or formate, are often used. After evaporation of solvent and buffer, the mixture of peptides and enzyme is chromatographically and/or electrophoretically separated into individual components. (*Electrophoresis* is a method of resolving mixtures based on differing mobilities of dissolved ions under the influence of an electric field. See Section A–3.)

In contrast to acid hydrolysis, enzymatic cleavage does not result in destruction of tryptophan or in hydrolysis of the side-chain amide functions of glutamine and asparagine residues.

Trypsin and chymotrypsin are the two endopeptidases most widely used for cleaving large peptides for sequence determination. Use of these two enzymes provides the overlapping fragments necessary if the sequences of the individual fragments are to be placed in their proper order.

Carboxypeptidase action is a more economical method for determination of C-terminal residues than is hydrazinolysis (Section 5-2). However, the exopeptidases continue their action without waiting for the experimenter to identify each liberated amino acid, and they do not attack all terminal residues at the same rate. Therefore, even if the action of carboxypeptidase is not halted by a residue resistant to its action, the sequence of only a limited number of residues may be established. This is carried out by determining the different amino acids liberated as a function of time of incubation.

CHEMICAL CLEAVAGE   Chemical methods for specific cleavage of peptide bonds are of recent development. The most specific of these methods are oxidative in nature. They make use of intramolecular nucleophilic attack by a peptide carbonyl on an unsaturated side chain that has been activated by reaction with an electrophilic reagent. The intermediates that result are hydrolyzed to break the peptide chain. Examples are given in Figure 4–2. Cleavage by N-bromsuccinimide (or bromine) in aqueous solution has been shown to occur at peptide bonds involving tyrosine and tryptophan carboxyls, as shown in Figure 4–2, and also, presumably by a similar path, at peptide bonds to which histidine contributes the carboxyl function. Although the order of ease of cleavage appears to be try > tyr > his, it is not possible to restrict the reaction even to the most reactive of these. Bromine and N-bromosuccinimide are also capable of oxidizing other amino acid residues, notably those with sulfur-containing side chains.

On the other hand, the cyanogen bromide cleavage of methionyl peptide bonds (Figure 4–2) appears to be specific for that residue, and is now widely used.

Peptide bonds formed with the amino groups of serine and threonine are particularly susceptible to cleavage under acidic conditions. This susceptibility probably results from $N \to O$ acyl migration to form the hydrolytically more labile ester [Eq. (4–8)]. The $N \to O$ acyl transfer, induced by acid, is common to N-acyl-1,2-amino alcohols; the reverse process, $O \to N$ migration, occurs when the amino group is not blocked by a proton. $N \to O$ acyl migration in a peptide or protein may be brought about with minimal rupture of other peptide bonds by storage in very strong acids (concentrated sulfuric, anhydrous hydrogen fluoride), but more aqueous media are

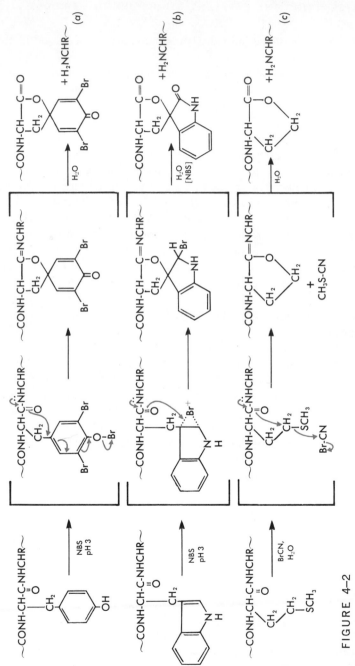

FIGURE 4–2

Selective oxidative peptide cleavage at (a) tyrosine, (b) tryptophan, and (c) methionine residues. NBS is N-bromsuccinimide.

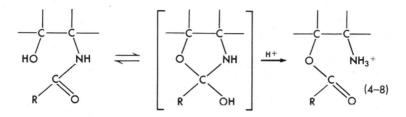

(4-8)

required to complete the cleavage by hydrolysis of the esters formed. Under mildly acidic conditions (aqueous acetic acid or dilute solutions of stronger acids), aspartic acid is liberated from proteins and peptides. The mechanism of this process is not clear.

4-5 Structure Determination of Proteins

Enzymes and many chemical reagents do not fully attack protein molecules unless the latter can be converted from their normally folded structures (see Chapter 5) to linear random chains. For this to be possible it is necessary to break disulfide cross links, if they are initially present, before digestion. Rupture of disulfide bridges may be carried out by oxidation with performic acid, which converts cystine and cysteine residues to those of cysteic acid (the corresponding sulfonic acid), as shown in [Eq. (4–9)]. A milder course utilizes

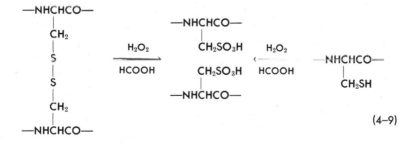

(4-9)

reduction, for which mercaptoethanol is a useful reagent [Eq. (4–10)], followed by alkylation with, say, iodoacetamide [Eq. (4–11)]. Structural information is lost in this manner, but the lost information, that is, the position of cross links, can be recovered once the sequence of the protein is known. This is done by isolation of cystine-containing peptide fragments from unoxidized (or unreduced) starting material. The amino acid compositions of these fragments are

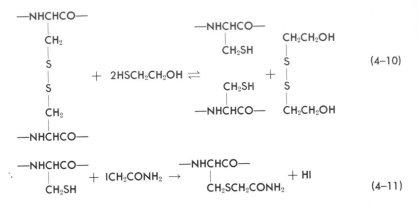

$$(4\text{--}10)$$

$$(4\text{--}11)$$

determined and matched with those of half-cystine-containing regions in the established sequence to indicate which of the half-cystine residues are interconnected.

Another problem is posed by the occurrence of both asparagine and aspartic acid and glutamine and glutamic acid in proteins. Which residues have free carboxyls and which have carboxamido side chains is established by examination of peptides (obtained by papain or subtilisin digestion) that give only one residue or glutamic or aspartic acid on acid hydrolysis. If acid hydrolysis of one of these peptides liberates ammonia, the amide form of the side chain was present, and this information can be incorporated into the overall sequence.

Using the techniques outlined in this chapter, the structures of numerous naturally occurring peptides have been established. In Figure 4–3 is shown the scheme by which the amino acid sequence of a tridecapeptide was established. The peptide shown is α-MSH (melanocyte-stimulating hormone), a hormone isolated from pituitary glands (see Section 6–1). The scheme illustrates, perhaps better than words, the reasoning involved in determining a peptide sequence. About 7 micromoles (about 10 milligrams) of peptide was used.

Table 4–1 lists some proteins for which the amino acid sequence has now been completely determined. Which proteins are studied depends very much on their availability and ease of purification. Something like 100 micromoles, which for a 15,000 molecular weight is 1.5 grams, of extremely pure protein is currently required for sequence determination.

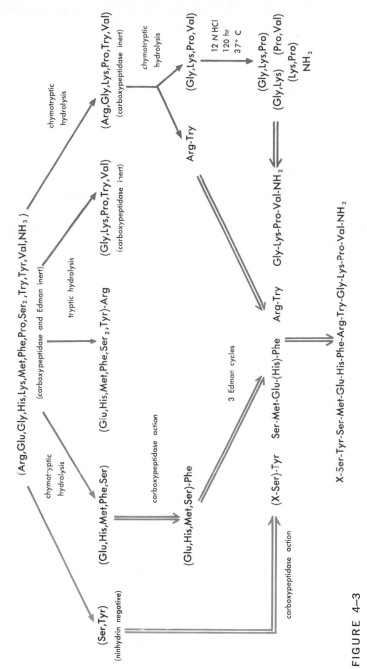

FIGURE 4-3

Scheme used to determine the sequence of the tridecapeptide hormone α-MSH. X was found to be acetyl. Double arrows indicate conclusions from evidence.

TABLE 4–1 ■

Some Proteins of Known Amino Acid Sequence

Protein	Number of residues	Function
Insulin[a]	51[b]	Hormone affecting sugar metabolism (Sec. 6–1)
Ribonuclease	124	Enzyme that catalyzes hydrolysis of phosphoric ester links in ribonucleic acid
Cytochrome c[a]	104[d]	Enzyme important to biological oxidation-reduction processes
Tobacco mosaic virus protein	158	2100 of these units make up the protein coat of the virus
Lysozyme	129	Enzyme that catalyzes hydrolysis of certain β-glycosides
Hemoglobin[a,c]	140,146[d]	Oxygen-carrying pigment of blood (Sec. 6–3)
Chymotrypsinogen	246	Precursor of peptidase, chymotrypsin (Sec. 6–2)

[a] These proteins have been obtained from a number of different species. Their sequences differ from species to species.
[b] In two chains connected by disulfide bridges.
[c] Two of the 140-unit and two of the 146-unit chains make up the protein part of the molecule.
[d] Position of porphyrin prosthetic groups also established.

4–6   Fingerprinting Peptides

If a linear peptide chain is completely digested by trypsin, it is converted to a mixture of peptides containing one more peptide than the number of lysine and arginine residues in the chain. A two-dimensional separation of these peptides on paper, using electrophoresis in one direction and partition chromatography in the other, yields what is called a *peptide map* or *fingerprint*.

Similar proteins from different species may differ in the replacement of a few amino acid residues (see Chapter 6); these related proteins may not always be distinguishable by available separation techniques. However, replacement of a single residue in one of the peptides produced by trypsin-catalyzed hydrolysis is likely to cause that tryptic fragment to take up a different position on a peptide map. Because of this, peptide mapping is a sensitive method for determining the identity of two proteins. If the maps of two similar proteins (one of known sequence) are compared, the variant peptide fragments in the other can be identified. These can be separated for sequence determination and fitted into the remaining known sequence. A complete new sequence study is thereby avoided.

References

Reviews

R. E. Canfield and C. B. Anfinsen, "Concepts and Experimental Approaches in the Determination of Primary Structure of Proteins," in H. Neurath (ed.), *The Proteins*, Vol. I, 2nd ed., Academic Press, New York, 1963, pp. 311–378.

J. P. Greenstein and M. Winitz, "Sequential Analysis of Peptides," in *Chemistry of the Amino Acids*, Vol. 2, Wiley, New York, 1961, Chap. 16, pp. 1512–1687.

R. L. Hill, "Hydrolysis of Proteins," *Advan. Protein Chem.*, **20**, 37–107 (1965).

C. H. W. Hirs, "The Chemistry of Peptides and Proteins," *Ann. Rev. Biochem.*, **33**, 597–672 (1964).

B. Witkop, "Nonenzymatic Methods for the Preferential and Selective Cleavage and Modification of Proteins," *Advan. Protein Chem.*, **16**, 221–321 (1961).

Paper

E. Bricas, J. van Heijenoort, M. Barber, W. A. Woestenholme, B. C. Das, and E. Lederer, "Determination of Amino Acid Sequences in Oligopeptides by Mass Spectrometry. IV," *Biochemistry*, **4**, 2254–2260 (1965).

5

▪ CONFORMATION OF PEPTIDE CHAINS

THE SPATIAL ARRANGEMENT of the atoms in a molecule is known as its *conformation*. A molecule may retain the same covalent framework and yet exist at different times in different conformations. A particular conformation is specified by the equilibrium bond lengths and angles of the covalent bonds present, *plus* the relative positions of groups that are nominally free to rotate about single bonds. For most molecules, including peptides, many conformations satisfying the requirements of the covalent framework are possible. Which conformations are more stable, and by how much, is determined by the sum of many noncovalent interactions among individual atoms and groups.

It has proved useful to discuss the structure of proteins and large peptide molecules at several levels. *Primary structure* is the arrangement of covalent bonds, that is, the information indicated by the usual structural formulas. (Primary structure determination was outlined in Chapter 4.) What are called the secondary and tertiary structures of a peptide describe its conformation. *Secondary structure* is the spatial relationship of near neighbors along the peptide chain. *Tertiary structure* is gross folding of that chain, which may bring into proximity in space parts of the molecule otherwise widely separated along its backbone.

The chemical, physical, and biological properties of a protein depend as much on secondary and tertiary structure as they do on amino acid sequence. When the conformation of a protein is altered from that of its native state, loss of biological function usually occurs; this phenomenon is known as *denaturation*.

5–1   Geometry of the Peptide Bond

The geometry of peptide bonds is of prime importance in defining possible conformations of peptide chains. Physical data, especially from X-ray crystallographic studies, have indicated that the preferred arrangement of atoms in a peptide bond is the planar, *trans* configuration, with bond angles and distances close to those indicated in Figure 5–1. Coplanarity of the C_α—C=O and C_α—N—H groups is the result of resonance stabilization,

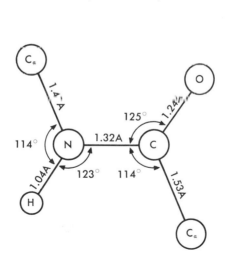

FIGURE 5–1

Average dimensions of the peptide bond.   All atoms shown lie in one plane.

which requires *p*-orbital overlap and sp^2 hybridization of nitrogen and carbonyl carbon atoms. Evidence for this resonance is the C—N bond distance, about 1.32 A, greatly shortened from the normal C—N single-bond distance, 1.47 A. The bond lengths shown in Figure 5–1 correspond to about 30 and 70 per cent double-bond character for the C—N and C—O bonds, respectively.

In rotation from *trans* to *cis* geometry, an amide bond must pass through a state in which C_α—C═O and C—N—H parts are in perpendicular planes. In this intermediate state, overlap between carbonyl π and nitrogen *p* orbitals is impossible, and the resulting loss in resonance energy is the major barrier to rotation (see Figure

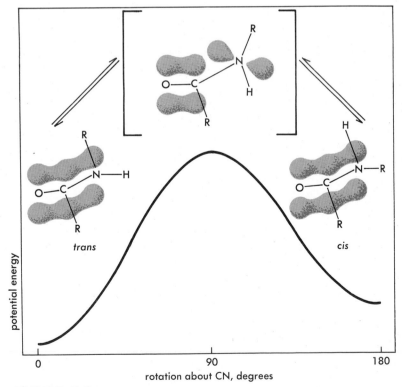

FIGURE 5–2

The barrier to rotation about the peptide bond.

5-2). Studies of the rate at which *N*-substituents of amides change position (using nuclear magnetic resonance spectroscopy) indicate that this barrier is at least 10 kilocalories per mole.

Although open-chain monosubstituted amides exist in the *trans* form (Figure 5-1) in the crystalline state, equilibrium between *cis* and *trans* configurations is possible in solution. The *trans* form is favored, but the precise position of the equilibrium is not known. Destabilization of the *cis* form probably arises from nonbonded repulsion of the groups represented by C_α in Figure 5-1, and so the preference for *trans* is likely to be of the same order as the difference in stability between *trans*-1,2-dialkylethylenes and their *cis* isomers, or 1 to 3 kilocalories per mole.

5-2 Interamide Hydrogen Bonds

One factor strongly influencing the preferred conformations of peptide chains is formation of hydrogen bonds between nearby peptide linkages. A hydrogen bond A—H· · ·B is an attraction between two closely spaced electronegative atoms with a proton between them. The hydrogen end of a covalent bond between hydrogen and an electronegative atom bears a partial positive charge. This charge is not well-shielded from its surroundings and can be attracted toward an unshared pair of electrons belonging to a nearby second electronegative atom (Figure 5-3). The strongest hydrogen bonds are formed when the proton involved lies on a line between atoms of nitrogen, oxygen, or fluorine.

Hydrogen bonds in crystalline substances are inferred to exist when shortened A—H· · ·B distances are found by X-ray crys-

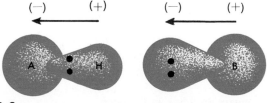

FIGURE 5-3

A hydrogen bond is the result of an attraction between two dipoles, one formed by the A—H bond and the other produced by atom B and a pair of its unshared valence electrons.

tallographic studies.   X-ray work has clearly demonstrated that crystalline amides form intermolecular hydrogen bonds between nearby C=O and N—H groups, and that hydrogen bonding is an important factor in determining the manner in which amide molecules are packed in a crystal lattice.   The average value of N—H· · ·O distances in crystalline amides is 2.93 A, whereas an estimate of the sum of the van der Waals radii of nitrogen and oxygen atoms, based on examination of other substances, is 3.05 A.

Evidence of hydrogen bonding is also obtained from infrared and proton magnetic resonance spectra, from changes in the acidity of the A—H groups, and from studies of bulk properties that are affected by molecular association.   Such studies indicate that intramolecular hydrogen bonding of monosubstituted amides occurs not only in the solid state, but when they are dissolved in solvents that do not themselves form hydrogen bonds, like benzene or carbon tetrachloride.   In such solvents the formation of a single amide-amide hydrogen bond, Eq. (5–1) for example, results in a favorable heat of formation ΔH, of -3 or -4 kilocalories per mole.

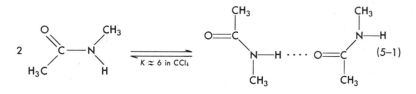

In a solvent such as water, which is itself highly associated through hydrogen bonds, the extent of association between amide molecules is small and is influenced by interactions between solvent and the less polar parts of the molecule.   (For N-methylacetamide [Eq. (5–1)] the equilibrium constant in water has been estimated at 0.005.) Intermolecular hydrogen bonds between amide molecules are not favored in aqueous solution, because, if water has unrestricted access to the amide unit, hydrogen bonds of at least equal strength may be formed between water and the amide. ΔH for formation of an interamide hydrogen bond in water appears to be close to zero.

5–3   Secondary Structure in Peptides

Conformations are not known for all peptides; indeed, for many peptides strongly preferred conformations may not exist.   However, some forms of secondary structure, presumed to be rather general, have been identified in those proteins and peptides in which there are extended regions of repeating structural regularities. These materials include some of the fiber-forming proteins and, under appropriate conditions, most synthetic amino acid polymers of sufficiently high degree of polymerization.

About 1951, Linus Pauling and Robert B. Corey proposed for peptides a group of secondary structures that have received much experimental support. They assumed that the peptide bond has the structure of Figure 5-1, and that each C=O group forms a hydrogen bond with an N—H group, with the hydrogen atom no more than 30° off the line joining the oxygen and nitrogen atoms. In their models they held the conformations about C—C and C—N single bonds at close to the rotational potential energy minima. They also required that all amino acid residues in the chain give rise to the same progression in space, and took into account the requirement for close packing that is the result of the ubiquitous van der Waals forces. These assumptions generated chains folded into helical conformations when all amide-amide hydrogen bonds were intrachain, and sheet-like structures when they occurred between chains.

HELICAL CONFORMATIONS   The most satisfactory helical structure calculated by Pauling and Corey is known as the α-helix and is illustrated in Figure 5-4. In the α-helix, the peptide backbone forms a coil with a pitch (distance between turns) of 5.4 A, and a progression along the axis of that coil of 1.5 A per amino acid residue (3.6 residues per turn). Hydrogen bonds are formed between C=O and N—H groups four residues apart, forming rings of 13 atoms, exclusive of hydrogen. This secondary structure has been found to describe the conformations, both in the solid state and in solution, of a large number of peptides and parts of some proteins. (It is not the only helical conformation that has been observed, however, and is sometimes assigned without sufficient evidence.) In general, it appears that when an α-helix is formed, residues of the L-amino acid series prefer to form a right-handed one.

The α-helix has been identified by X-ray diffraction in some forms of solid synthetic poly(amino acids) such as poly(L-alanine) and poly(γ-methyl-L-glutamate). These peptides show evidence of a repetitive atomic spacing of 1.5 A, difficult to explain on any other basis. The α-helix is also consistent with data from the ordered regions found in some fibrous proteins, such as the α-keratins of

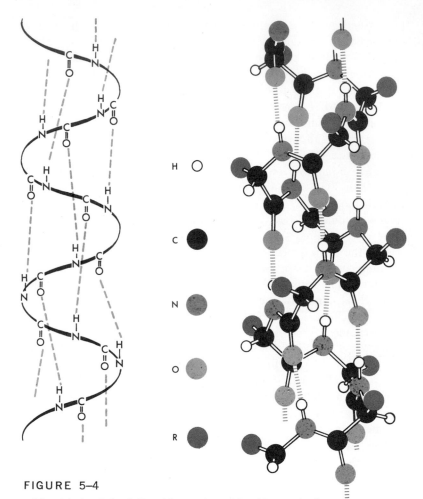

FIGURE 5–4

The right-handed α-helix with L-amino acid residues. A schematic representation is given at the right.

hair and wool. Oriented fibers of these materials absorb polarized infrared light in a manner indicating that the C=O and N—H bonds are aligned with the long axis of the molecule, a finding consistent with a helical structure, though not necessarily the α-helix (see Figures 5–4 and 5–5). The dimensional parameters of helical structures of amino acid polymers in solution have been characterized by light scattering and low-angle X-ray scattering, by viscosity versus

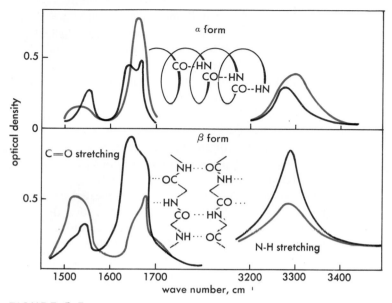

FIGURE 5–5

Infrared dichroism of stretched poly(L-alanine) films. The long dimensions of the peptide molecules tend to line up in the direction of stretching. When the electric vector of plane-polarized light is aligned with the C=O or N H dipole, absorption is maximal at the corresponding vibrational stretching frequency. The solid line was obtained in each case with the electric vector perpendicular to the direction in which the films were stretched; the colored lines were measured when it was parallel.

molecular-weight determinations, and by other techniques that pro-vide information about the over-all shape of large molecules. (Note that an ideal peptide helix is a rod of calculable diameter and length, the latter depending linearly on chain length.) Recently, the α-helix has been shown, by X-ray crystallography, to be a major form of structural regularity in crystals of a globular (soluble) protein, the oxygen-carring pigment myoglobin (Section 5–5).

EXTENDED STRUCTURES   Helical structures are apparently not stable conformations of amino acid polymers with certain branched side chains, such as poly(L-valine), or of those that have heteroatoms attached to the β-carbon atom, like poly(L-serine). These polymers are more stable in conformations that permit interchain hydrogen

bonds to exist.   [It should be noted that poly(L-proline), which cannot form amide-amide hydrogen bonds, does take up helical conformations, an indication that hydrogen bonding is only one of several forces that determine secondary structure.]

Of structures that can be written for a regular array of peptide
chains with maximal interchain hydrogen-bond formation, two appear most reasonable.   In one, the peptide chains are fully extended,
with all the atoms of the backbone lying in a plane; hydrogen bonds
are formed between chains running side by side in opposite directions
(antiparallel).   An amino acid residue extends about 7.2 A along the
axis of a fully extended chain.

In the second extended structure, known as the pleated sheet, there
is rotation about the bonds to the α-carbon atom, so that the C—H
bond is in the plane of an adjacent amide group, *trans* to the N—H
and C=O groups nearest it (see Figure 5–6).   Hydrogen bonds can
be formed between parallel or antiparallel chains.   The repeat distance along the axis of the backbone for structures of this type is near
6.7 A.

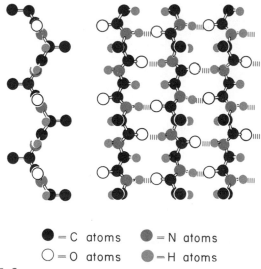

● = C atoms   ● = N atoms
○ = O atoms   ● = H atoms

FIGURE 5–6

*A peptide β-structure, the antiparallel pleated sheet.   At left is a view of on
chain through the mean plane of the sheet.*

Extended peptide secondary structures, generally known as β-structures, have been identified in films and fibers of synthetic poly(amino acids), as already mentioned. In the case of poly(L-alanine), it is possible to convert the helical form (known as the α-form) to an extended β-form by stretching (see Figure 5–5). β-Peptide structures have also been identified in silk fibroin, the protein of silk. Large peptide molecules are not soluble when intramolecularly associated in sheet-like structures, but β-structures have been suggested for some dissolved amino acid polymers of relatively low degree of polymerization.

5–4 Hydrophobic Bonds

A phenomenon known as *hydrophobic* (or *apolar*) *bonding* may be a major force in establishing stable conformations of peptide molecules dissolved in water. Hydrophobic bonding tends to stabilize conformations in which hydrocarbon residues are maximally removed from contact with water molecules, and is a reflection of the fact that hydrocarbons are not very soluble in water.

Water is a unique solvent, in that its molecules associate strongly through formation of several intermolecular hydrogen bonds each. Dissolved hydrocarbon residues interfere with this association, and cause water molecules in their immediate vicinity to arrange themselves in a more ordered manner. When two or more hydrocarbon residues can come together, some of the ordered water molecules surrounding them are released to the more disordered state of the bulk solvent [Eq. (5–2)]. This process, illustrated graphically in

$$n[\text{hydrocarbon } (H_2O)_x] \rightleftharpoons (\text{hydrocarbon})_n + nxH_2O \qquad (5\text{–}2)$$

Figure 5–7, may or may not have a favorable heat of reaction, but it does produce a sufficiently favorable entropy change to ensure that its equilibrium lies to the right.

Calculations and experiments with model substances indicate that the strength of a single hydrophobic bond, formed as in Figure 5–7, is slight, perhaps 1 to 2 kilocalories per mole in terms of free energy. However, the number of hydrophobic interactions possible in a protein molecule, in which perhaps 30 per cent of the amino acids may have apolar side chains, is great, and the stabilization to be ob-

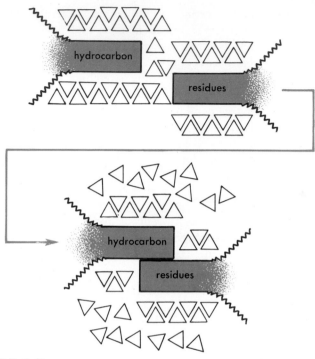

FIGURE 5–7

Hydrophobic bond formation. The triangles represent water molecules. On approach of the hydrocarbon residues to each other, some of the water molecules are released from an ordered arrangement close to hydrocarbon to a more disordered state in bulk solvent.

tained by optimization of this form of bonding can be large. There also is an additional importance to hydrophobic bonding in that it can bring about chain folding that tends to exclude water from the peptide backbone. It has already been noted (Section 5–2) that amide-amide hydrogen bonds are not favored in aqueous solution. By providing a nonaqueous environment for parts of the peptide backbone, the hydrophobic interaction can permit hydrogen bonds between peptide links to act in stabilizing ordered secondary structures.

5–5 The Structure of Myoglobin

The most detailed information yet obtained about the secondary and tertiary structure of a large peptide, and confirmation of the importance of the factors just discussed, has come from an X-ray crystallographic determination of the structure of (sperm whale) myoglobin, an oxygen-carrying pigment of muscle. This protein contains 153 amino acid residues in a single peptide chain, to which is also bound the iron porphyrin prosthetic group, heme. A three-dimensional electron density map, at 1.5-A resolution, was obtained by analysis of the X-ray diffraction patterns produced by single crystals of myoglobin and several mercury-containing derivatives. This monumental task, carried out by John C. Kendrew and co-workers, has resulted in location of almost all the atoms (except those of hydrogen) in the molecule. The amino acid sequence so found agrees with that established by chemical means, and the folding of the molecule, which could not have been predicted from the amino acid sequence, is very clear. A schematic sketch of the myoglobin structure is given in Figure 5–8. Subsequent work has indicated that myoglobins of other species, although differing in amino acid composition, have substantially the same over-all structure.

About 75 per cent of the amino acid residues in myoglobin are found in helical segments that have spatial parameters in close agreement with predictions for the right-hand α-helix. Conformations about single bonds are close to those of the rotational potential energy minima. Most of the polar side chains are on the periphery of the molecule, in contact with the water molecules that make up about 40 per cent of the mass of the crystal. (Most of these water molecules are not sufficiently fixed in position to be resolved.) Two polar side chains, imidazoles of histidine residues, interact with the iron atoms of the largely buried heme group. Otherwise, the interior of the roughly spherical molecule contains the nonpolar, hydrophobic side chains, generally packed to distances determined by their van der Waals radii.

Crystallographic studies of other proteins are in progress, and an analysis at 2-A resolution of an enzyme from hen egg white, lysozyme, has been reported. The factors influencing its conformation are not so clear as in the case of myoglobin. In crystalline lysozyme only about 40 per cent of the 129 amino acid residues appear to be

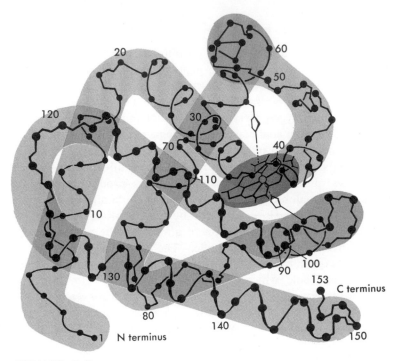

FIGURE 5–8

An outline of the myoglobin peptide backbone as revealed by X-ray crystal-lography.

included in helical segments, and several of the hydrophobic side chains are outside the interior of the roughly ellipsoidal molecule.

Although it is an open question whether the structure found for a large polypeptide molecule in its crystals is the same as its structure in solution, indications in the myoglobin case are that the two are similar. The observed tertiary structure of myoglobin (its over-all folding) seems to be determined, in the rather wet crystals examined, by the same hydrophobic and hydrophilic forces that would be acting on it if it were dispersed in solution. In addition, estimates of the helix content of dissolved myoglobin molecules, made on the basis of the optical rotatory dispersion and circular dichroism (Section 5–6) of myoglobin solutions, agree with the observed helix content of the crystalline material.

5–6   Amino Acid Polymers in Solution

Synthetic amino acid polymers are convenient models with which to evaluate the forces that contribute to secondary and tertiary structure in structurally more complex peptides and proteins. Study of these polymers in solution has largely revolved around aspects of the transition that can often be observed between an unstructured, random, highly solvated coil form and a regular helical form.

Changes between helix and coil conformations of dissolved amino acid polymers can be monitored by observation of changes in the optical properties of the solution. Several of these have been shown to correlate with the helix-coil transition. In the infrared spectrum, the carbonyl-stretching frequency reflects changes in the hydrogen bonds formed by that group; in the ultraviolet, there is a decrease in the intensity of the peptide bond absorption at 190 millimicrons when a helix is formed. Of great convenience are changes in the rotation of plane-polarized light.

When a randomly coiled peptide chain takes on a regular helical conformation, there is added a new asymmetric feature, over and above the α-carbon asymmetric centers of each amino acid residue. This new feature is the helix itself, which may be right- or left-handed, but is of the same sense in every chain. A helix is not superimposable on its mirror image, and, loosely speaking, the added over-all molecular asymmetry results in a further contribution to the rotatory power of the peptide. Not only does the rotation at a single wavelength change, but the shape of the *rotatory dispersion* curve, the curve describing rotatory power as a function of wavelength, also changes. From the constants describing this dispersion and suitable empirical correlations, it has been possible to estimate the helix content of peptides and proteins. A related tool, which provides potentially more information than the determination of optical rotatory dispersion, is the measurement of *circular dichroism*, the differences in absorption of left and right circularly polarized light.

For a known polypeptide solution the helix-coil transition may be detected merely by observing changes in optical rotation at a single wavelength, as a crucial parameter (for example, temperature, pH, or solvent composition) is varied.

HELIX STABILITY   Studies using amino acid polymers and copolymers in nonaqueous solvents indicate that weakly or nonhydrogen bonding solvents, such as chloroform and ethylene dichloride,

TABLE 5–1 ■

Helix Stability of Amino Acid Polymers

Side chain	Transition occurs at 25° in:[a]	
(CH₃)₂CH—	No helix	Increasing
C₆H₅CH₂OCOCH₂—	10% DCA in CHCl₃	helix
C₆H₅CH₂OCONH(CH₂)₄—	35% DCA in CHCl₃	stability
CH₃COOCH₂—	45% DCA in CHCl₃	
C₆H₅CH₂OCO(CH₂)₂—	70% DCA in CHCl₃	
(CH₃)₂CHCH₂—	10% TFA in DCA	
CH₃SCH₂CH₂—	10% TFA in DCA	
CH₃—	40% TFA in DCA	↓

[a] DCA = dichloroacetic acid; TFA = trifluoroacetic acid.

favor helix formation. Strongly proton-donating solvents, such as dichloroacetic and trifluoroacetic acids, disrupt the ordered structure to produce solvated random coils, presumably by disrupting intrachain hydrogen bonds. (Anhydrous trifluoroacetic acid has been shown to transfer protons completely to the peptide bond, and the resulting electrostatic repulsions may help to prevent helix formation in this solvent.) The stability of a helical secondary structure in mixtures of chloroform and dichloro- or trifluoroacetic acids is dependent on the nature of the side chains. Table 5–1 indicates the order of helix stability for some synthetic amino acid polymers. The relationship between side chains and helix stability is not entirely clear, although steric interference between side chains and solvent-side-chain interactions are probably involved.

Helical forms of common amino acid polymers are not soluble in water, but some measurements of the effect of side chains on helix stability in water have been made. It appears, for example, that the CH₃— and CH₃SCH₂CH₂— side chains of alanine and methionine exert a strong helix-stabilizing effect, consistent with stabilization by hydrophobic bonding, on water-soluble copolymers containing chiefly the glutamic acid-derived residue

—NHCHCO—
  |
  CH₂CH₂CONHCH₂CH₂ N   O

Alone, this residue forms a peptide that prefers the random-coil form in water.

A further nonbonded interaction, not yet mentioned but probably also important in establishing preferred conformations of peptides and proteins, is the electrostatic interaction of charged side-chain groups. Poly(L-glutamic acid) and poly(L-lysine) both unfold from helical to random-coil structures upon ionization in aqueous solvents. This unfolding is the result of electrostatic repulsion of like-charged groups and the high solvation requirements of those groups. The effects of the transition upon the optical rotation and viscosity of solutions of poly(L-glutamic acid) are shown in Figure 5–9.

COOPERATIVE EFFECTS   The helix–random-coil transition in an aqueous solution of poly(L-glutamic acid) is abrupt in comparison to changes in the degree of side-chain ionization (Figure 5–9). Each carboxyl group ionizes almost independently of its neighbors, but the formation of even a single turn of the helix requires cooperative action of many neighboring residues. Because of this cooperative

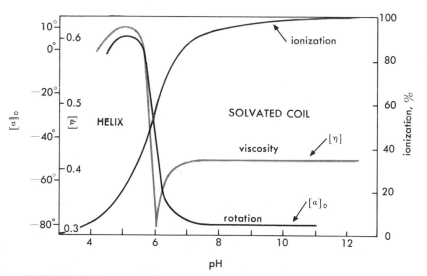

FIGURE 5–9

pH dependence of specific rotation, intrinsic viscosity, and degree of ionization of poly(L-glutamic acid) (average degree of polymerization, 260) in 1:2 dioxane– 0.2 M NaCl. Precipitation begins below pH 5.

nature, helix-coil transitions are generally sharp. Consider the α-helix. In this conformation each peptide bond is in part stabilized in its position by two hydrogen bonds, formed between it and peptide bonds three units along the chain on either side. For these stabilizing links to form, the units between the peptide bonds they join must already have been folded into the helical conformation. (This is true whether the stabilizing interaction between adjacent turns of the helix is hydrogen bonding or some other net attractive force.) Thus, if most of the chain is already in the helical form, it will be relatively easy for internal random regions to adopt that conformation; conversely, if most of the chain is in the random form, remaining helical regions will tend to disappear. Put another way, a helical segment is more stable between helical segments, and a random segment is more stable between random segments.

From the foregoing it can also be seen that the ends of peptide chains are less apt to exist in helical conformations. The lower the degree of polymerization of a peptide, the greater is the proportion of its residues near the chain ends. We can therefore expect a minimum chain length below which helical structures do not form. An estimate of this minimum has been obtained from the behavior of oligopeptides (prepared by stepwise synthesis). It appears to be about 10 or more units in favorable cases, but varies, of course, with solvent and the amino acid residues involved.

References

Reviews

C. H. Bamford A. Elliott, and W. B. Hanby, *Synthetic Polypeptides*, Academic Press, New York, 1956.

R. E. Dickerson, "X-Ray Analysis and Protein Structure," in H. Neurath (ed.), *The Proteins*, Vol. II, 2nd ed., Academic Press, New York, 1964, pp. 603–778.

W. Kauzmann, "Some Factors in the Interpretation of Protein Denaturation," *Advan. Protein Chem.*, **14**, 1–63 (1959).

E. Katchalski, M. Sela, H. I. Silman, and A. Berger, "Polyamino Acids as Protein Models," in H. Neurath (ed.), *The Proteins*, Vol. II, 2nd ed., Academic Press, New York, 1964, pp. 405–601.

E. Katchalski and M. Sela, "Synthesis and Chemical Properties of Poly-α-Amino Acids," *Advan. Protein Chem.*, **13**, 244–492 (1958).

F. M. Richards, "Structure of Proteins," *Ann. Rev. Biochem.*, **32**, 269–300 (1963).

H. A. Scheraga, "Intramolecular Bonds in Proteins, II. Non-Covalent Bonds," in H. Neurath (ed.), *The Proteins,* Vol. I, 2nd ed., Academic Press, New York, 1963, pp. 477–594.

J. A. Schellman and C. Schellman, "The Conformation of Polypeptide Chains in Proteins," in H. Neurath (ed.), *The Proteins,* Vol. II, 2nd ed., Academic Press, New York, 1964, pp. 1–137.

P. Urnes and P. Doty, "Optical Rotation and the Conformation of Polypeptides and Proteins," *Advan. Protein Chem.,* **16,** 401–544 (1961).

J. T. Yang, "Viscosity of Macromolecules in Relation to Molecular Conformation," *Advan. Protein Chem.,* **16,** 323–400 (1961).

Papers

C. C. F. Blake, D. F. Koenig, G. A. Mair, A. C. T. North, D. C. Phillips, and V. R. Sarma, "Structure of Hen Egg-White Lysozyme," *Nature,* **206,** 757–761 (1965).

G. Holzwarth and P. Doty, "The Ultraviolet Circular Dichroism of Polypeptides," *J. Am. Chem. Soc.,* **87,** 218–228 (1965).

■ SOME BIOLOGICAL ASPECTS OF PEPTIDE CHEMISTRY

THE ULTIMATE IMPORTANCE of the peptide chemistry outlined in the preceding chapters lies in its use as a tool to uncover and manipulate biological processes. Sections of this chapter illustrate briefly some of the uses to which peptide chemistry has been put in attacking biological and biochemical problems.

6–1   Peptide Hormones

POSTERIOR PITUITARY HORMONES   The first major triumph of synthetic peptide chemistry was the synthesis, in 1953, by Vincent duVigneaud and co-workers, of the posterior pituitary hormones *oxytocin* and *vasopressin*. These are nonapeptides with the structures

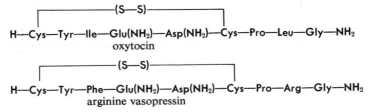

Oxytocin, among other effects, brings about contraction of uterine muscle to induce labor (oxytocic action). Vasopressin acts on the kidney to reduce excretion of water (antidiuretic action) and brings about a rise in blood pressure (hypertensive action). Each hormone exhibits some of the physiological effects of the other. Many synthetic analogs of oxytocin and vasopressin, containing replacements of one amino acid residue by another, have been prepared since 1953. Synthetic oxytocin and some analogs are used clinically, exchangeably with hormones isolated from animal pituitaries. The physiological activity of synthetic oxytocin and vasopressin analogs has been the subject of considerable study.

A noteworthy chemical feature of oxytocin and vasopressin is their cyclic structure, which is completed by a disulfide link. This ring is opened by reduction, and it can be quantitatively reclosed by oxidation, with complete recovery of the initial structure and physiological activity. Chemical synthesis of these hormones and their analogs proceeds through a linear nonapeptide, containing S-blocked cysteine residues that are unblocked and oxidized to the disulfide in the last steps (Section 3–7). This facile cyclization is one of a number of cases that suggest that peptides containing six amino acid residues tend to fold in a manner bringing the chain ends together [see also Eq. (3–61)].

ANTERIOR PITUITARY HORMONES   The anterior portion of the pituitary gland contains hormones that stimulate the cortex of the adrenal glands to production of cortical steroid hormones. One of these *adrenocorticotropic hormones* (*ACTH, β-corticotropin*) has been identified as a 39-residue linear peptide (Figure 6–1). The porcine variety of this peptide has now been totally synthesized, and the synthetic product is identical with the natural hormone in all chemical and physiological behavior.

Reference to Figure 6–1 indicates that $β$-corticotropins obtained from different species vary in only a part of the peptide chain. Presumably that part of the molecule remaining unchanged from species to species is central to the function of the peptide. The varying portion probably plays a more general role, perhaps in maintaining necessary secondary or tertiary structure. In the case of the corticotropins, essentially full physiological activity resides in the 20 N-terminal residues, which do not include the species variations. Synthesis and assay of N-terminal peptides in the corticotropin series indicate that activity first appears in peptides containing

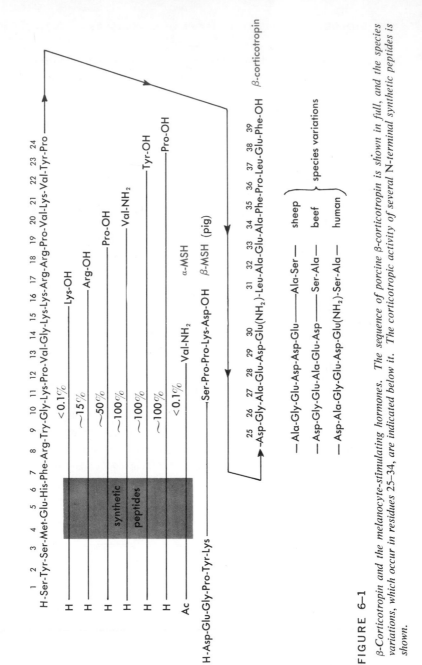

FIGURE 6–1

β-Corticotropin and the melanocyte-stimulating hormones. The sequence of porcine β-corticotropin is shown in full, and the species variations, which occur in residues 25–34, are indicated below it. The corticotropic activity of several N-terminal synthetic peptides is shown.

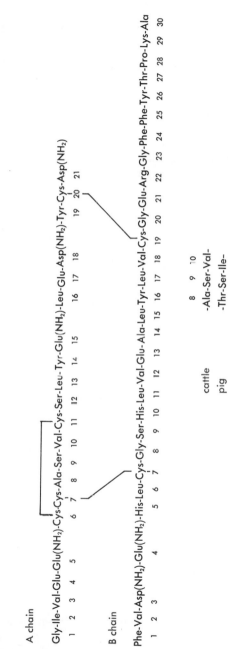

FIGURE 6–2

The primary structure of beef insulin. Species variations are indicated in the table below the sequence.

residues 1–13, and does not increase if residues beyond the valine at position 20 are added.

The corticotropically active peptides also act on melanocytes, pigmented cells of skin, causing them to darken. Naturally occurring *melanocyte-stimulating hormones* (α- and β-MSH) are related to corticotropin, and it appears that a particular heptapeptide sequence, residues 4–10 in the corticotropin structure, is necessary for MSH activity.

OTHER PEPTIDE HORMONES   Several physiologically active peptides are produced by action of enzymes on proteins present in blood plasma. These are synthetically accessible, and therefore have been, like the posterior pituitary hormones, the subject of intensive studies on the relationship between amino acid sequence and biological activity. Two of these may be mentioned: The *angiotensins* have hypertensive activity associated with the sequence

H—Asp—Arg—Val—Tyr—Ile—His—Pro—Phe—

Bradykinin, which is a hypotensive agent, has the sequence

H—Arg—Pro—Pro—Gly—Phe—Ser—Pro—Phe—Arg—OH

Two large peptide hormones are obtained from pancreas and have been completely identified. These regulate carbohydrate metabolism. *Glucagon* is a 29-residue linear peptide that causes an increase in blood sugar levels. *Insulin* brings about a decrease in blood sugar levels by stimulating storage of glucose as the poly-saccharide, glycogen.

Insulin is large enough to be ranked as a protein; its primary structure is shown in Figure 6–2. Species variations are confined to residues 8–10 of the shorter chain. By cleavage of the disulfide bridges, the two chains may be separated. Neither has physiological activity; both have now been synthesized. Reoxidation of a mixture of the two chains, natural or synthetic, affords a mixture of products with only 1 to 2 per cent of full activity, corresponding to random recombination.

6–2 Enzymes

Enzymes are proteins that catalyze chemical reactions in living systems. They are involved in all steps of the synthesis of proteins, carbohydrates, lipids and their precursors, in the oxidation of biological fuels and storage of the chemical energy so obtained, in the conversion of that chemical energy to other forms, and in the conversion of solar energy to chemical energy. Enzymes are of manyfold higher efficiency and specificity than man-made catalyst systems, and they operate under the restricted conditions of temperature, pH, etc., in which life exists.

A general mechanism of enzyme action may be stated as follows: The enzyme and its substrates combine to form an *enzyme-substrate complex*. Within this complex occur a series of atomic and electronic rearrangements, and the rearranged complex then decomposes to form products and free, regenerated enzyme. The net catalyzed reaction is one between the substrates; what the enzyme protein does is to provide a favorable intramolecular environment for a reaction that would otherwise require near simultaneous collision of several molecules. It serves to combine the substrates, and such of its own functional groups as are catalytically useful, all in a geometry favorable to reaction.

Much recent effort in the study of enzyme chemistry has been devoted to the identification of the details of the mechanisms by which enzymes exert their catalytic action. Perhaps the best understood enzyme in this respect, to date, is the peptidase, chymotrypsin.

CHYMOTRYPSIN   Chymotrypsin is elaborated by the pancreas in the form of an inactive precursor, chymotrypsinogen. The 246–residue amino acid sequence of the single peptide chain of bovine chymotrypsinogen is known and is shown schematically in Figure 6–3. In the small intestine, where active enzyme is used, chymotrypsinogen is enzymatically activated. α-Chymotrypsin, the form of the enzyme most studied, is produced by enzymatic hydrolysis at the four points indicated in Figure 6–3; it therefore consists of three chains, linked by two disulfide bridges, and it contains three disulfide-closed intrachain loops. The tertiary structure of chymotrypsin is not known; it appears to contain considerably less helix than does myoglobin (Section 5–5).

Normal substrates for chymotrypsin are peptides of aromatic amino acids, but the enzyme will also bring about hydrolysis of simple *N*-acyl aromatic L-amino acid esters and amides, for example *N*-acetyl-L-tyrosine ethyl ester:

$$EtO \text{---} COCHCH_2C_6H_5OH$$
$$| $$
$$NHCOCH_3$$

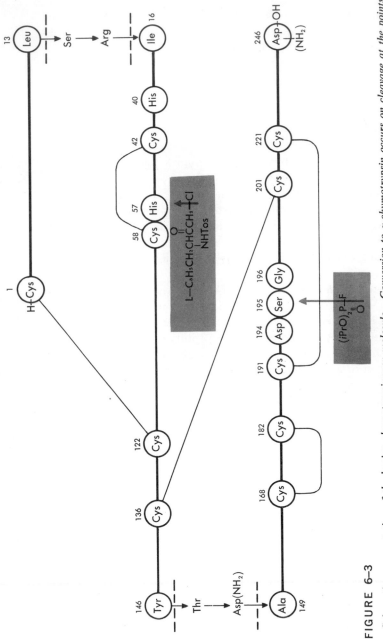

FIGURE 6–3

Schematic representation of the bovine chymotrypsinogen molecule. Conversion to α-chymotrypsin occurs on cleavage at the points indicated by the dashed lines. The disulfide bridges are indicated by light lines between the cysteine residues. Diisopropylphosphofluoridate destroys enzymatic activity by reaction at the hydroxyl of serine 195. L-1-toluenesulfonamido-2-phenylethyl chloromethyl ketone alkylates the imidazole ring of histidine 57.

Chymotrypsin reacts irreversibly with 1 mole of diisopropyl-phosphofluoridate, $(i\text{PrO})_2\text{P(O)F}$, to form a phosphoryl ester devoid of hydrolytic activity. The presence of acetyl-L-tyrosine ethyl ester prevents phosphorylation, suggesting that phosphorylation occurs in the vicinity of the so-called active site of the enzyme. The inhibiting phosphoryl group has been, in fact, located in the peptide chain of the enzyme. This has been accomplished by partial hydrolysis of the phosphorylated protein, followed by isolation and identification of the peptide fragment containing phosphorus. The phosphorus is found attached to the hydroxymethyl side chain of the serine residue at position 195 (Figure 6–3); this serine residue, of the 28 present, is thus identified as part of the active site. Considerable evidence has been collected to support the ideas that, during catalysis, it is temporarily acylated by the carboxyl part of a normal substrate, as indicated in Eq. (6–1).

$$\text{ChTr—OH} + \text{RCOX} \rightarrow \text{ChTr—O—COR} + \text{HX}$$

$$\downarrow \text{H}_2\text{O}$$

$$\text{ChTr—OH} + \text{RCOH}$$

(6–1)

The presence also of an imidazole group at the active site of chymotrypsin has been inferred from the pH-dependence of chymotryptic activity. Direct evidence has been obtained by reaction of the enzyme with an alkylating agent of the same general shape as a normal substrate [Eq. (6–2)]. The alkylated residue has been estab-

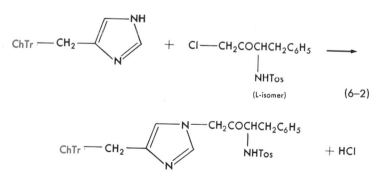

(6–2)

lished as the histidine at position 57 (Figure 6–3), and this reaction, like the phosphorylation of serine 195, results in loss of the enzymatic catalytic activity.

The serine at position 195 and the histidine at 57 are on two different peptide chains. Since both are involved in the catalytic action of chymotrypsin, the active site must be an interchain feature produced by the tertiary folding of the whole molecule. Because of the disulfide ring of residues 42–58, the histidine at position 40 is also part of the active region, and there are data to suggest that its imidazole side chain also participates in the catalytic process.

On the basis of the features just described, plus the results of extensive kinetic studies of chymotrypsin-catalyzed reactions, reaction mechanisms have been proposed to explain chymotrypsin action. They will not be detailed here, except to note that they propose the hydroxyl of serine 195 as a nucleophile in the first step of the process indicated in Eq. (6–1), and water as a nucleophile in the second step. The side-chain imidazole groups of the two histidines are suggested as agents for transferring protons to and from the other reactants.

The initial binding of chymotrypsin to its substrates probably occurs by hydrophobic bonding. An estimate of the shape of the region of the protein in which this occurs is being made by study of the reaction of the enzyme with a wide range of compounds, of varying molecular shape, that can act as substrates or inhibitors.

6–3 Hemoglobin

Hemoglobin is the oxygen-carrying pigment of red blood cells. It is a conjugated protein of molecular weight about 65,000, to which are bound four molecules of heme (ferrous protoporphyrin IX, Figure 6–4), one associated with each of four peptide chains. In normal adult human hemoglobin the chains are of two types, two identical chains of 141 residues (called α) and two identical chains of 146 residues (called β). The complete amino acid sequences of the two types of chain are known, and the shape of the whole molecule to 5.5-A resolution has been determined by X-ray crystallography. In the complete molecule the four peptide chains are arranged tetrahedrally (Figure 6–5). (The arrangement of individual, noncovalently bound peptide chains associated in a single protein molecule is called *quaternary structure.*)

A number of abnormal human hemoglobins are known. Their biosynthesis is an inheritable trait that may or may not be associated with clinical symptoms. Abnormal hemoglobins have the same four-chain gross structure as normal hemoglobin but differ by the

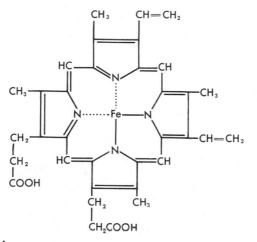

FIGURE 6–4

Ferrous protoporphyrin IX.

replacement of a single amino acid residue. Some of the observed substitutions are shown in Figure 6–6.

It is reasonable to expect that only those substitutions that do not interfere seriously with the tertiary structure of either chain will exist; otherwise synthesis of the whole hemoglobin molecule would not occur. From this point of view, it is interesting to note that most of the substitutions are of one hydrophilic side chain for another. Although the detailed three-dimensional structure of hemoglobin chains is not yet known, there appears to be considerable parallel between the folding of the hemoglobin α- and β-chains and that of the single chain of myoglobin (Section 5–5). Judged by this similarity, it seems that most of the substitutions in Figure 6–6 occur in positions at the outside of the folded chains, and not in positions that could affect the helix formation and hydrophobic bonding which determine the tertiary structure.

One hereditary disease associated with an abnormal hemoglobin is sickle-cell anemia. In this form of anemia red blood cells maintain their normal shape in the presence of sufficient oxygen, but become misshapen and are destroyed under conditions of oxygen deficiency. The phenomenon is associated with the presence of hemoglobin-S,

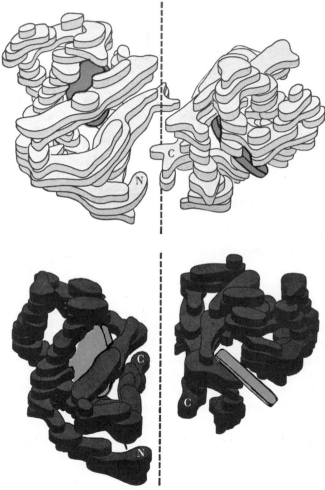

FIGURE 6–5

Quaternary structure of hemoglobin.   Two α-chains (top) and two β-chains (bottom) are represented here by electron-density contours at 5.5-A resolution. In the complete molecule the α-chains are inverted and placed in the space between the β-chains.   The colored disks represent the porphyrin rings associated with the protein.   [Reproduced with permission from *Sci. Am.*, **211** (5), 73 (1964).]

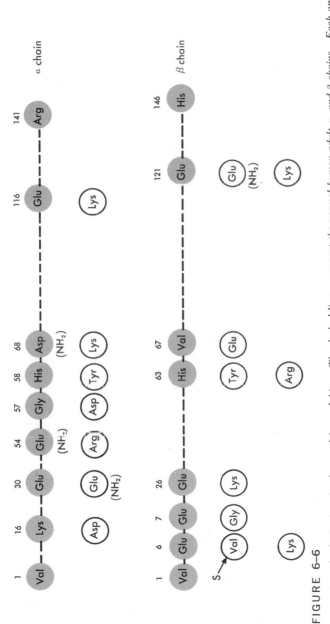

FIGURE 6–6

Amino acid substitutions in abnormal hemoglobins. The dashed lines represent the normal human adult α- and β-chains. Each amino acid symbol off the lines indicates replacement observed in an abnormal hemoglobin. The symbols on the lines indicate the normal residues in the positions where replacements have been observed to occur. Position numbers increase from the N-terminus.

in the β-chain of which a hydrophilic glutamic acid residue has been replaced by one of valine, which has a hydrophobic side chain. It is interesting to speculate that this replacement does not sufficiently affect the tertiary structure of the β-chain to prevent formation of the hemoglobin molecule, but that what changes it does produce may be sufficient to affect the manner in which hemoglobin molecules pack in a red blood cell. X-ray studies indicate that the positions of the four parts of a normal hemoglobin molecule change slightly on going from the oxygenated to deoxygenated state. A small change in tertiary structure, induced by the replacement of valine for glutamic acid, could then result in a gross change in the shape of the contents of the red cell on deoxygenation.

6–4 Peptides from Microorganisms

Lower organisms, bacteria and fungi, synthesize proteins based on the common amino acids, but they frequently also produce smaller peptides containing unusual structural features. Some of the peptide-like products of microorganisms are shown in Figure 6–7. They range from straightforward cyclic peptides such as the *tyrocidins* and *gramicidins* (components of the topical antibiotic mixture tyrothricin), which depart from "normal" structures only in the presence of a residue of the D optical series, to the *penicillin* and *cephalosporin* antibiotics, which are perhaps peptides only by courtesy. The peptide chain of *valinomycin*, an antibiotic that has some activity against the tubercle bacillus, contains ester groups and α-hydroxy acids as part of its backbone. Peptides such as this, condensed in part through links other than the peptide bond, are known as *depsipeptides*.

Other antibiotics shown in Figure 6–7 include a *polymyxin*, one of a group of antibiotics based on α, γ-diaminobutyric acid, and an *actinomycin*. The actinomycins are of particular interest because of their cytostatic activity; they damage proliferating cells, as do X-rays, and are therefore of interest in cancer chemotherapy.

A toxic principle of the death cup mushroom (*Amanita phalloides*) is *phalloidin*. It appears to kill by interference with the energy-requiring syntheses of proteins and polysaccharides. The ergot alkaloids (for example, *ergotamine*) are produced by a fungus (*Claviceps purpurea*) which grows on rye plants. Ergotamine is used as an oxytocic and in the treatment of migraine. The peptide portion of

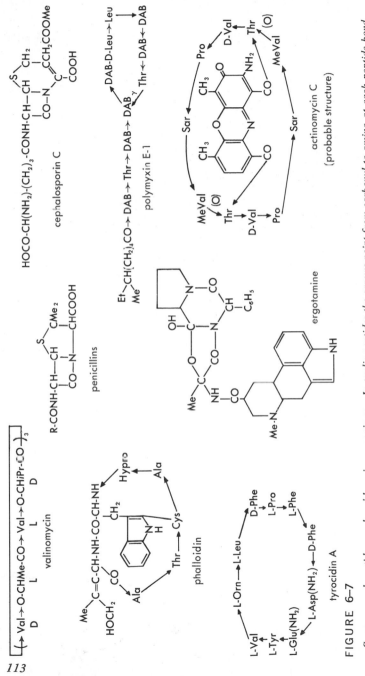

FIGURE 6-7

Some unusual peptides produced by microorganisms. In cyclic peptides the arrows point from carbonyl to amino at each peptide bond.
DAB is α, γ-diaminobutyric acid; MeVa⁺ is N-methylvaline; Sar is sarcosine.

113

114   ■ PEPTIDES AND AMINO ACIDS

ergotamine includes an acyl-phenylalanyl-prolyl sequence in which an amide N—H group has added across a nearby carbonyl group. This so-called cyclol structure has been suggested as a common feature for all peptides, but evidence of its widespread occurrence is lacking.

References

Books and Reviews

M. L. Bender and F. J. Kézdy, "Mechanism of Action of Proteolytic Enzymes," *Ann. Rev. Biochem.*, **34**, 49–76 (1965).
P. D. Boyer, H. Lardy, and K. Myrbäck (ed.), *The Enzymes,* 2nd ed., Academic Press, New York, 1959–. Volume I treats general properties of enzyme-catalyzed reactions; subsequent volumes deal with individual classes of enzymes.
G. Braunitzer, K. Hilse, U. Rudloff, and N. Hilschmann, "The Hemoglobins," *Advan. Protein Chem.*, **19**, 1–71 (1964).
M. Dixon and E. C. Webb, *Enzymes,* 2nd ed., Academic Press, New York, 1964. A textbook.
A. R. Fanelli, E. Antonini, and A. Caputo, "Hemoglobin and Myoglobin," *Advan. in Protein Chem.*, **19**, 74–222 (1964).
K. Hofmann and P. G. Katsoyannis, "Synthesis and Function of Peptides of Biological Interest," in H. Neurath (ed.), *The Proteins,* Vol. I, 2nd ed., Academic Press, New York, 1963, pp. 53–188.
W. P. Jencks, "Mechanism of Enzyme Action," *Ann. Rev. Biochem.*, **32**, 639–676 (1963).
D. E. Koshland, Jr., "Correlation of Structure and Function in Enzyme Action," *Science,* **142**, 1533–1541 (1963).
C. Niemann, "α-Chymotrypsin and the Nature of Enzyme Catalysis," *Science,* **143**, 1287–1296 (1964).
R. Schwyzer, Chemistry and Metabolic Action of Non-Steroid Hormones," *Ann. Rev. Biochem.*, **33**, 259–286 (1964).

Papers

M. L. Bender, J. V. Killheffer, Jr., and F. J. Kézdy, "The Active Site of Chymotrypsin," *J. Am. Chem. Soc.*, **86**, 5331–5333 (1964).
M. Bodanszky and D. Perlman, "Are Peptide Antibiotics Small Proteins?" *Nature,* **204**, 840–844 (1964).
J. Buettner-Janusch and R. L. Hill, "Molecules and Monkeys," *Science,* **147**, 836–842 (1965). Studies of primate evolution using changes in hemoglobin primary structure.

E. B. Ong, E. Shaw, and G. Schoellman, "An Active Center Histidine Peptide of α-Chymotrypsin," *J. Am. Chem. Soc.,* **86,** 1271–1272 (1964).

Popular Articles

H. Neurath, "Protein-Digesting Enzymes," *Scientific American,* December 1964, pp. 68–79.

M. F. Perutz, "The Hemoglobin Molecule," *Scientific American;* May 1964, pp. 64–76.

▪ APPENDIX: SEPARATION OF AMINO ACID AND PEPTIDE MIXTURES

IF THE ONLY METHODS available for separating mixtures of organic compounds were the classical techniques of distillation, crystallization, and extraction, very little could be accomplished in peptide synthesis or sequence determination. Such work requires techniques that are adaptable to very small quantities and can distinguish nonvolatile, chemically sensitive molecules that differ only slightly in size, composition, polarity, and solubility. *Chromatographic* procedures have proved most valuable, but *electrophoresis*, which resolves mixtures on the basis of ionic mobilities, and *gel filtration*, which separates molecules on the basis of size, are also important.

In a chromatographic separation, as in fractional distillation, the components of a mixture are continually distributed between two phases that move relative to one another. Each component tends to move with that phase for which it has the greater affinity, at a rate corresponding to its preference for that phase.

A–1 Solvent-Solvent Partition Methods

The equilibrium distribution of a solute between two immiscible liquid phases is described by the ratio of its concentrations in the two phases; this ratio is known as the *partition coefficient*. It is dependent on the solute, the two phases, and the temperature, and is concentration independent at low solute concentrations. If the partition coefficient of one substance between two given phases is very large, and that of another, between the same two phases, very small, the two may be completely separated in a simple one-step distribution process, such as that carried out in a single separatory funnel.

COUNTERCURRENT DISTRIBUTION   If the partition coefficients of two substances are not very different, separation may still be achieved by distribution between two immiscible solvents, but a multistep process, using a number of separatory funnels and a number of different portions of the two phases, is required. The multistep process is known as *countercurrent distribution*, and is illustrated in Figure A–1. The closer the two partition coefficients, the more distribution steps are required to obtain a given degree of separation. If only a few steps are required, a countercurrent distribution may be carried out by hand, using a rack of separatory funnels. Frequently, however, many transfers must be made, and automatic equipment, available up to the equivalent of 500 separatory funnels, is used. This equipment has been quite useful in purifying both natural products and synthetic peptides.

PARTITION CHROMATOGRAPHY   Partition chromatography may be considered a countercurrent distribution process carried out, not in discrete steps, but in a continuous flow process. One of the liquid phases is immobilized on a hydrophilic support such as cellulose or silica gel, and the other is percolated through a bed of the supported phase. For amino acid and peptide separations, the two phases are usually obtained from a single homogeneous solvent mixture containing water. In contact with this mixture, the hydrophilic support surrounds itself with a film of relatively high water content, and the distribution of solutes occurs between this film and the bulk solvent. The more organic-soluble components tend to travel with the moving solvent, and the more water-soluble components tend to be held back by the stationary film. The solvent mixture chosen is one in which the components of the mixture have a small solubility. If the latter are too soluble they will all travel with the velocity of the bulk solvent; if too insoluble, they will not be moved at all.

When macro separations are to be performed, partition chromatography may be carried out using a column of the supported sta-

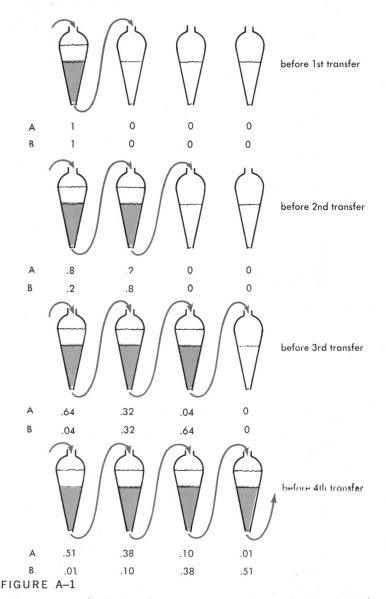

				before 1st transfer
A	1	0	0	0
B	1	0	0	0

				before 2nd transfer
A	.8	.2	0	0
B	.2	.8	0	0

				before 3rd transfer
A	.64	.32	.04	0
B	.04	.32	.64	0

				before 4th transfer
A	.51	.38	.10	.01
B	.01	.10	.38	.51

FIGURE A–1

Countercurrent distribution of a two-component mixture. Component A is four times as soluble in the upper phase as it is in the lower phase (colored). B is one-fourth as soluble in the upper phase as it is in the lower. The upper phase remains stationary; the lower phase is moved one funnel to the right after each equilibration. Fresh lower phase is added to the funnel at the left at each transfer. Assuming that equal volumes of the two solvents are used, the numbers indicate the fraction of the initial charge of each component present in each funnel. Sufficient further transfers would result in complete separation of A and B.

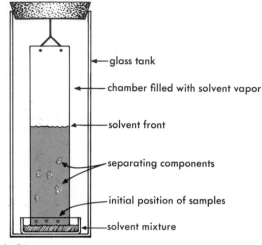

glass tank

chamber filled with solvent vapor

solvent front

separating components

initial position of samples

solvent mixture

FIGURE A–2

Simple apparatus for ascending paper chromatography using paper strips.

tionary phase. Thin sheets of supports are conveniently used when micro quantities are to be separated, as in analytical work.

In *paper chromatography* a small amount of the mixture to be separated is absorbed, usually as a circular spot, near one end of a strip of filter paper, and the end of the paper near the spot is dipped into the solvent mixture. To develop the chromatogram, the solvent is allowed to run, by capillarity, past the initial spot and on up or down the filter paper. So that the composition of the flowing solvent remains constant throughout development, the strip is held at constant temperature in a chamber saturated with vapors of the developing solvent. (Figure A–2 illustrates one way of carrying out the paper chromatographic process.) Before the front of the advancing solvent reaches the end of the paper, the strip is dried and the separated components detected. If separation has been complete, the individual components will be detected as circular spots displaced to varying distances from the origin. The ratio of the distance a substance has traveled in the direction of solvent motion to the distance traveled by the solvent front itself is known as the R_F value.

Table A–1 lists a number of solvent systems commonly used in

TABLE A–1 ■
R_F Values of Some Amino Acids

Substance	Solvent[a]			
	1	2	3	4
Glycine	.33	.41	.25	.03
Alanine	.39	.60	.32	.05
Leucine	.72	.84	.58	.31
Phenylalanine	.66	.85	.59	.38
Tyrosine	.53	.51	.64	.19
Serine	.31	.36	.28	.02
Aspartic acid	.33	.19	.22	.00
Lysine	.18	.81	.14	.01
Histidine	.19	.69	.28	.03

[a] Solvents: (1) 1-Butanol (4 parts), acetic acid (1 part), water (4 parts); the upper layer of the mixture is used; (2) phenol (4 parts), water (1 part); (3) 2,4,6-collidine (125 parts), water (44 parts); (4) 1-butanol (1 part), benzyl alcohol (1 part), saturated with water and in the presence of diethylamine vapor.

paper chromatography of amino acids, together with R_F values of a few representative substances. Since R_F values are dependent on temperature, exact solvent composition and the batch of paper used, the values given in the table are only indicative.

The amount of material that may be handled on a paper chromatogram is quite small, usually a matter of micrograms. Use of larger quantities may overload the capacity of one or both phases, resulting in poor separation. Milligrams of material may be separated, especially if thick paper is used, by painting the mixture as a narrow band, perpendicular to the direction of solvent flow, near one end of a large sheet. The components are then resolved as a series of bands that may be cut apart so that each may be eluted.

Paper chromatography is particularly useful in identifying and determining the purity of amino acids and peptides. If two substances have identical R_F values when chromatographed together in several solvent mixtures, they may be presumed identical. A substance that affords a single spot no matter what solvent system is used for development is very likely to contain only one molecular species.

Mixtures that are not resolved by a single solvent mixture may often be resolved by *two-dimensional paper chromatography*. In

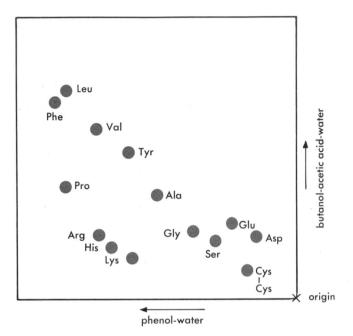

FIGURE A–3

Separations produced on a two-dimensional paper chromatogram of a mixture of amino acids.

this procedure, the initial mixture is placed as a spot at one corner of a sheet of paper and the chromatogram developed with one solvent. The paper is then dried, rotated, and the second solvent made to flow at right angles to the first. Figure A–3 indicates the separation of a mixture of amino acids by two-dimensional paper chromatography.

Thin-layer chromatography is a versatile technique very similar in operation to paper chromatography, differing in that the stationary phase and its support rest as a layer of fine particles on an inert backing. Many different stationary phases may be used, and thin-layer chromatography is not only adaptable to solvent-solvent partition separations but also to separations based on absorption, ion exchange, and gel filtration. It has an additional advantage in that it may be carried out quite rapidly.

DETECTION OF AMINO ACIDS AND PEPTIDES   If, as is frequently the case, the components of a chromatographically separated mixture are not colored, it is necessary to locate their position on the chromatogram by some additional operation. The separated materials may be identifiable by fluorescence or ultraviolet absorption. If they are radioactive they may be located by localized fogging of a photographic plate held against the chromatogram. Frequently chemical treatment of the developed chromatogram is used to render the components visible. A wide variety of color tests can be used for amino acids and peptides, and some of these are listed below:

Ninhydrin produces colors if primary aliphatic amino groups are present [Eq. (2–22)]. 0.2 micrograms of an amino acid may be detected.

Chlorination of amides by treatment of the paper with chlorine vapor,

$$—CONH— + Cl_2 \rightarrow —CONCl— + HCl$$

followed by subsequent reaction with starch-iodide,

$$—CONCl— + 2\,I^- + H^+ \rightarrow —CONH— + I_2 + Cl^-$$

is a general method for detecting peptides.

Diazonium salts couple with the aromatic rings of tyrosine and histidine residues to produce colored azo compounds (Pauly test).

Iodoplatinate ion, PtI_6^{2-}, is reduced by sulfur-containing residues (cystine, methionine) to form light spots on a dark background.

Dimethylaminobenzaldehyde condenses with the indole ring of tryptophan under acid conditions to form colored products (Ehrlich test) [Eq. (A–1)].

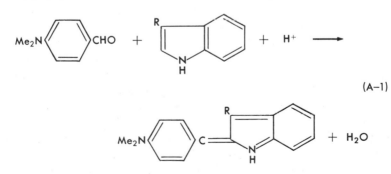

(A–1)

α-Naphthol and hypochlorite react with guanidine functions (arginine) to give red products of unknown structure (Sakaguchi test).

Since these color tests are destructive, they cannot be used if components of the mixture are to be recovered. In preparative paper chromatography, where the components are separated as bands across the paper, the necessary reagents are applied to only a narrow strip to locate the bands to be eluted.

A–2 Ion Exchange Chromatography

Displacement chromatography on ion exchange resins is one of the most effective ways of resolving mixtures of amino acids and peptides with high recoveries, on a large or small scale (see Section 4–1). Ion exchange resins are organic polymer networks, swollen with water, that incorporate ionic groups as part of their structure. In *cation exchangers*, negatively charged groups are attached to the polymer, and the necessary balancing positive ions are free to move in the surrounding solvent. In *anion exchangers*, the reverse is the situation. The most commonly used ion exchange resins are based on copolymers of styrene with 2 to 8 mole per cent of divinylbenzene, a cross-linking agent. In cation exchangers the ionic groups are usually sulfonic acid functions, and in anion exchangers they are quaternary ammonium groups.

To illustrate the ion exchange process, consider a column packed with a bed of sulfonic acid resin particles. If a solution of sodium chloride is passed through the column, sodium ions will displace the hydrogen ions initially associated with the resin; hydrochloric acid will be eluted from the column. Divalent cations are more tightly bound than univalent cations, and if a solution of a calcium salt is run through the column in its sodium salt form, the sodium ion will be displaced from the column. These processes are not irreversible. Although hydrogen ion is less tightly bound to the resin than sodium or calcium ions, the resin can be reconverted to its original hydrogen form by running sufficient acid through the column. Processes of this sort are widely used in softening water (replacing calcium and magnesium ions by sodium ions) or deionizing it (by replacing cations with hydrogen ion and anions with hydroxide ion).

In acid solution amino acids and many peptides are cations; their amino groups are protonated and the ionization of their carboxyl groups is suppressed. As cations they have a tendency to be retained in association with the sulfonate ions of cation exchangers, but they may be displaced by other cations. At a given acidic pH, other things being equal, the component of a mixture with the smallest tendency to carry a positive charge will be displaced most readily. The situation for chromatography on anion exchangers is analogous: Amino acids and peptides are bound to these in equilibrium with an alkaline solution, and the substances with the least tendency to carry a negative charge are most readily displaced.

The tendency of an amino acid or peptide to be bound to an ion exchange resin is not entirely determined by its degree of ionization. In any separation on an ion exchange resin there are elements of partition chromatography between the bulk buffer solution and the solvent within the resin particles. Absorption to the surface of the resin itself may also play a part. Aromatic amino acids, for example, are preferentially retained by polystyrene resins.

Separation of amino acids on cation exchangers is an analytical tool of prime importance and was discussed at greater length in Section 4–1. For proteins and peptides, ion-exchanging cellulose derivatives have proved more useful than polystyrene-based exchangers. The most common of these are carboxymethylcelluose (CM cellulose) and diethylaminoethycellulose (DEAE cellulose), which are prepared by etherification of a small fraction of the hydroxyl groups of the cellulose. Above pH 3 the former is a cation exchanger and below pH 10 the latter is an anion exchanger. Use of these materials is frequently combined with a gradient-elution technique, in which the pH and/or concentration of the eluting buffer is continuously and smoothly varied as development proceeds.

A–3   Electrophoresis

Migration of charged particles in an electric field is known as *electrophoresis*. The rate at which a dissolved ion migrates under the influence of an electric field is determined, on the one hand, by the charge on the ion and, on the other, by viscous forces retarding its motion through the solvent. The charge on an amino acid or peptide molecule depends on pH and on the ionization constants of the functional groups present. The viscous forces are a function of the shape of the ionized solute molecule and its degree of solvation. Roughly speaking, the higher the charge on the ion and the smaller it (plus its solvation shell) is, the faster it will move.

To utilize differences in ionic mobilities for a chemical separation,

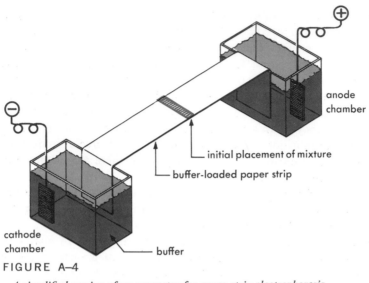

FIGURE A–4

A simplified version of an apparatus for paper-strip electrophoresis.

a volume of buffer solution is placed between two electrodes, and the mixture to be separated is introduced to a small part of this volume, usually midway between the electrodes, in a manner that avoids mixing with the bulk of the buffer solution. When a voltage is impressed across the electrodes, the components of the mixture migrate, the distance each travels in unit time being proportional to its mobility. At an appropriate point, before the ions of interest have reached the electrodes, the field is turned off. The separated components are the detected and/or removed from their new positions in the buffer solution. It is obvious that achievement of any separation by this method requires that mechanical or convective mixing in the buffer be prevented. In electrophoretic separations of peptides the buffer is immobilized, to prevent mixing, by absorbing it into filter paper or cellulose acetate strips for small-scale separations (micro- to milligram quantities), or by incorporating it in gels formed by neutral polymers (polysaccharides or polyacrylamide) or absorbing it in a block of cellulose powder when larger quantities are to be separated. Figure A–4 indicates schematically an apparatus for electrophoretic separations on paper strips.

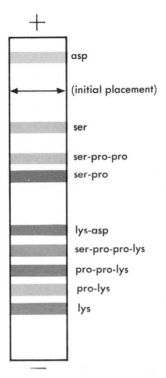

FIGURE A–5

Electrophoretic separation of a partial acid hydrolyzate of a peptide. The pH was 3.5, the field strength about 40 volts/cm, and the time required for separation 2 hours.

Electrophoresis on paper or cellulose acetate strips is used in peptide chemistry for the separation and identification of amino acids, determination of the purity of synthetic peptides, and separation of peptides produced by hydrolysis in amino acid sequence studies (Section 3–4). Figure A–5 illustrates the sort of separations attainable. The mixtures are placed in a band at the center of the strip and separate to give a series of bands that may be detected (Section A–2) and eluted for further purification or analysis as necessary. Separations require a matter of hours. Electrophoresis may also be used as one dimension of a two-dimensional paper chromatogram.

A–4   Gel Filtration

Gel filtration is a chromatographic process that differentiates molecules on the basis of size, using a stationary phase that behaves as *molecular sieve.*
Linear polymers are soluble in solvents that interact strongly enough with the units of which they are composed. In a cross-linked polymer, however, solvation may occur, but the individual chains cannot be dispersed; they can spread only as far apart as the cross links will allow, forming an expanded three-dimensional

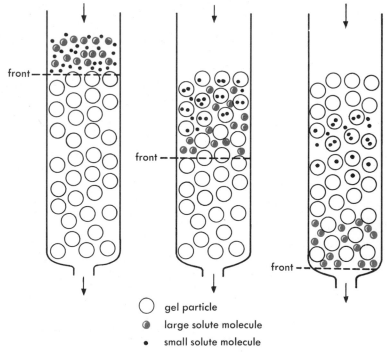

○   gel particle
◉   large solute molecule
•   small solute molecule

FIGURE A–6

A representation of the gel filtration process. The smaller molecules, which can enter the gel particles, have a larger volume to pass through than do the larger molecules, and are therefore eluted more slowly.

network. If cross links are frequent enough, solvation and the resulting swelling are severely restricted. If cross links are more widely spaced, not only small solvent molecules, but larger dissolved species are able to enter the pores of the polymer network, but sufficiently large molecules will still be excluded; thus the polymer acts as a molecular sieve.

In a chromatographic column packed with bulk solvent and beads of a solvent-swollen cross-linked polymer there will be present two volumes: the solvent between the particles and the solvent within the particles. Small molecules can travel freely in both volumes; large molecules will see only the volume of bulk solvent. If a mixture of small and large molecules is washed through the column, the column will appear to possess a smaller volume for the large molecules and these will be eluted first. The process is illustrated in Figure A–6.

By varying the frequency of cross links it is possible to vary the size of molecules excluded from the swollen polymer network. Ion exchange resins (Section A–3) behave to a certain extent as molecular sieves; chromatographic separations using them depend somewhat on their degree of cross linking. Organic polymer gels of cross-linked poly(methyl methacrylate) or polystyrene, which swell in organic solvents, may be used for grading organic-soluble substances on the basis of size. For peptides and proteins, however, gels that swell in water are desirable. These are provided by acrylamide-N,N'-methylenebisacrylamide copolymers or by cross-linked dextrans. Dextran is a polyglucoside produced by certain bacteria; it can be cross linked by reaction of some of its hydroxyl groups with epichlorohydrin [Eq. (A–2)].

$$2ROH + ClCH_2CH \overset{O}{\diagdown} CH_2 \xrightarrow{\ NaOH\ } RO-CH_2CHCH_2-OR \qquad (A-2)$$

Dextran and polyacrylamide gels are prepared to exclude completely molecules larger than molecular weight 1000 (smaller molecules can be excluded under some conditions), and they are available with exclusion limits up to 200,000. The more loosely cross-linked gels can be used to fractionate proteins, and the more tightly cross-linked ones for separation of peptides or peptides from proteins. Dextran gels with ion-exchange properties are also used for fractionations.

DIALYSIS   Dialysis is an older molecular-sieve technique useful in purification of proteins. A membrane (such as one of cellulose), impermeable to large molecules, divides two solutions but allows solvent and small molecules to diffuse freely between them. Regenerated cellulose membranes are impermeable to molecules of molecular weight above about 30,000, a limit that may be varied by chemical or mechanical treatment.

References

Books and Reviews

R. J. Block, E. L. Durrum, and G. Zweig, *A Manual of Paper Chromatography and Paper Electrophoresis,* 2nd ed., Academic Press, New York, 1958.

H. Determann, "Chromatographic Separations on Porous Gels," *Angew. Chem., Intern. Ed.,* **3,** 608–617 (1964).

J. P. Greenstein and M. Winitz, "Chromatography," in *Chemistry of the Amino Acids,* Vol. 2, Wiley, New York, 1961, Chap. 15, pp. 1366–1511.

E. Heftmann (ed.), *Chromatography,* Reinhold, New York, 1961.

E. Stahl (ed.), *Thin-Layer Chromatography, a Laboratory Handbook,* Academic Press, New York, 1965.

C. Wunderly, *Principles and Applications of Paper Electrophoresis,* Elsevier, New York, 1961.